COMPASS-WISE
OR
GETTING TO KNOW YOUR COMPASS

COMPASS-WISE

OR

GETTING TO KNOW YOUR COMPASS

BY

J. KLINKERT, F.R.I.N.

GLASGOW
BROWN, SON & FERGUSON, LTD.
52 DARNLEY STREET

First Edition - - 1976

© J. KLINKERT, 1976

ISBN   0 85174 252 1

BROWN, SON & FERGUSON, LTD., GLASGOW G41 2SG
Printed and Made in Great Britain

PREFACE

A NUMBER of professional seafarers have expressed the wish that a series of articles, written under the general title of 'Compass-Wise' and published in the journal *Safety at Sea International*, should be published in book form. The series to date is submitted herewith by the kind permission of Mr. H. A. Prince, M.R.I.N., Editor of *Safety at Sea International*.

The several essays remain substantially the same as the original articles though the sequence has been altered to improve the continuity. It is hoped that the professional navigator, as well as the amateur, will accept the appeal which is made to become Compass-Wise in a practical sense and perhaps encourage him to assume the character of a Compass Doctor, able to diagnose magnetic disturbances and prescribe the necessary remedies.

J. KLINKERT,
Hindhead.
June, 1976.

CONTENTS

CHAPTER 1

Do you Consider the Magnetic Compass to be a Museum Piece?

Due to prejudice and ignorance the magnetic compass, in its handsome teakwood binnacle is often openly despised by navigators. For them it has been superseded by a modern gyro installation, housed on the bridge in an imposing console and divested of all mystery.

WHILST Section 2 of the Merchant Shipping Act 1964 as expressed in terms of The Merchant Shipping (Passenger Ship Construction) Rules 1965 and The Merchant Shipping (Cargo Ship Construction and Survey) Rules 1965 specifies the minimum compass requirements aboard ship the fact remains that practising navigators often hold views about compass equipment which are prejudiced one way or another.

Magnetic or Gyro?

To the question, 'Which do you prefer—a magnetic or gyro compass?' the answer almost invariably lies in favour of the gyro. Asked 'Why?' the reasons given are that either this instrument is 'steadier', or that 'the errors are always small'. Few navigators, at first thought, attribute to the gyro installation the obvious benefits which it provides with distant reading repetition, the control of the auto-helm and the stabilisation of radar and W/T D/F. These more pertinent advantages are usually stated as after-thoughts.

Unsolved Mysteries

A number of ship's officers, if encouraged to express their views, tend to consider the magnetic compasses on board as more or less museum pieces, accepted with tolerance, sometimes amusement, rarely affection and seldom very seriously. Occasionally the magnetic compass is openly despised and thought to be superfluous in the presence of the more modern, sophisticated, and trouble-free (?) gyro installations. The gyro compass, often housed in an imposing console, eclipses the

1

apparently dated magnetic compass in its traditional teakwood binnacle. It is not difficult to trace the origin of such prejudices. In the first place the gryo is more impressive and arguably easier to use; in the second, the magnetic compass holds a time-honoured (and very real) mystery which most navigators are reluctant and even frightened to penetrate. In fact, many deliberately refuse to have anything to do with the thing. They lock it up securely and put the keys in the safe where no one can get at them.

Although compass theory and its relation to practice may have been understood by senior officers at the time of their professional examinations, the knowledge then gained is seldom used subsequently, and frequently forgotten; so, the mystery remains.

False Impressions

Prejudice and ignorance go hand-in-hand. Some marine navigators are surprised to be reminded that aircraft compasses are essentially magnetic compasses and therefore subject to the same theory of deviation as marine magnetic compasses. It comes as a disappointment to learn that gyro compasses as used on ships and controlled by the force of gravity in sensing tilt due to the earth's rotation cannot be used by aircraft because of the high speeds at which they fly, and because of the many horizontal accelerations which they experience.

For example, a marine-type gyro compass aboard a jet aircraft flying west across the North Atlantic at 580 knots along the 50th parallel would possess no directive property of and by itself. It follows that if ships are ultimately to travel and manoeuvre much faster in the future (hovercraft are a case in point) then some of the very familiar gyro compasses in use today will need to be replaced by stabilising gyros, monitored by the earth's magnetic field, in a manner similar to those used in aircraft. The ship's officer does well therefore, neither to prevent his prejudice from degrading the magnetic compass nor to allow his natural pride in the gyro to endow it with virtues it barely possesses.

Some Comparisons

Having established a sense of proportion the case for the gyro compass seems to predominate. The facility which it provides for monitoring auxiliary equipment such as distant repeaters, auto-helm, radar and W/T D/F has remained until recently the principal advantage to be gained from a gyro installation.

Now that the Transmitting Magnetic Compass (TMC) provides a similar service the gyro can no longer claim to be exclusive in this respect. Apart from the individual cost of the two kinds of installation it is still necessary to examine, from the user's point of view, the remaining differences which exist. Is, for instance, the gyro compass steadier than a well-corrected magnetic compass fitted with a transmission system? The general answer is, paradoxically, no.

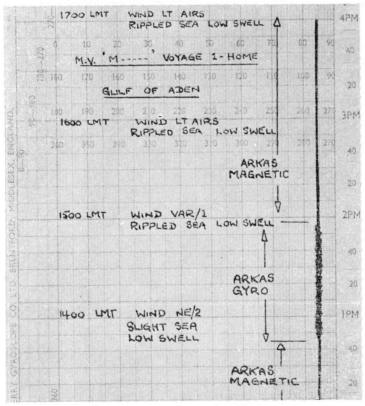

FIG. 1

The illustrated course recording provides some evidence which shows that under certain conditions a ship can be steered more effectively with a magnetic compass. Does the gyro indicate the true north/south direction more effectively than the magnetic compass? The answer is undoubtedly, yes; because the inevitable embarrassment of magnetic variation, which changes substantially with geographic location and time, is probably the most annoying feature of the magnetic compass to navigators aboard ship. Even the use of a Variation Setting Control (VSC) does not eliminate the inherent deficiency. The possibility of making a mistake of sign when using it can occur and the effect could be disastrous, as was indeed the case with an aircraft some years ago.

Finally, the real effectiveness of the magnetic compass presupposes that its proper correction for deviation is frequently updated. In practice this is seldom done by the navigators on board for reasons of traditional inertia and prejudice. or even ignorance. In the event the matter is delegated to a professional adjuster at irregular intervals and the conscience satisfied that nothing need be done between times provided the intervals are not too great. Defence for this procedure has been made that adjustments effected by an uncertificated compass adjuster would not be supported under enquiry in the event of an accident; this is a view held by some which is entirely without foundation.

Accuracies

Even if care was more constantly exercised in the matter of maintaining near-zero deviations the success is unlikely to be better than half of one degree. It is unlikely also, that the navigator or compass adjuster is able to observe deviation itself more closely than half of one degree. Furthermore, the magnetic variation at sea is unlikely to be known to within another half of one degree and frequently considerably more when regard is given to magnetic earth anomalies, diurnal changes, magnetic storms and other unpredictable sources of inaccuracy.

It seems, therefore, that although the modern magnetic compass is required to settle within one-tenth of a degree of the ambient field the direction of the latter can only be ascertained to within half of one degree or more at any instant of time. A tentative accuracy for heading reference and bearing accuracy using a well-adjusted magnetic compass is therefore unlikely to exceed 1° under the best conditions, and then only at the time of observation. Most commercial gyro compasses aim for an accuracy of one half degree but under severe test conditions such instruments exhibit an error of $1\frac{1}{2}°$

or more. This shows that although on balance the gyro equipment receives greater acceptance by marine navigators it is not necessarily more accurate. It is also true that modern types of marine gyro compasses require effectively no shipboard maintenance. The advent of the Sperry Marks 27, 30, 37 and 227, the Sperry Rand 120 (formerly the Japanese TKS ES series) and the Arma Brown have reduced shipboard maintenance almost completely. Although many ships in service still carry Sperry Mk E 14 and Brown types A and B, where some maintenance is required, both have now ceased manufacture in this country.

Heading and Bearing Reference

Over a period of time the gyro installation would appear to provide heading and bearing reference to within $1\frac{1}{2}°$ between astronomical checks whilst the magnetic compass provides accuracy of a similar order at the time of checking and an unknown degree of accuracy between times in those areas where the charted variation cannot be relied upon. The TMC exhibits a similar accuracy except that ancillary equipment which is monitored by it suffers enormously if unsteadiness caused by *inclination errors* are allowed to persist.

Heading Reference

The accuracy and efficiency of compass installations aboard ship are still further affected by displaced lubber lines. When steering and making courses these errors may become cumulative to the order of $2\frac{1}{2}°$ or more so that both magnetic and gyro installations are seldom able to define the *ship's head* with reference to the true meridian closer than 3° or 4°! Assuming a possible error in the heading reference of 3° from all sources it would account for a displacement from the mean intended track of over one nautical mile after a run of only 20 miles. During a day's run in the open ocean this could well account for a displacement of between 10 and 15 miles from the intended track which might otherwise be conveniently attributed to the set of imagined currents.

Practising navigators may well care to be 'Compass-Wise' more critically along the lines stated and not to subscribe to a particular type of installation, either magnetic or gyro, virtues which it may well not possess. It is certain that all compass systems require the most careful checking at intervals appropriate not just to the type of system but to the area being navigated.

CHAPTER 2

Error East - Compass Least!

Are you a slave to a rule or a rhyme? Here is an invitation to break with tradition, remove some misunderstandings and, perhaps, ensure greater safety.

THERE can be no fundamental topic of compass-work which has been more needlessly complicated, misrepresented and confused than that of the practice of applying the compass error and the deviation. To any professional or amateur navigator one of the first items of study is the proper correction of courses and bearings, and in this connection it would seem that the simplicity of doing this has been and still continues to be obscured by the use of rules and rhymes designed to aid the memory. The apparent necessity for using a rule, a rhyme, or any other aid to memory arises from the mistaken idea that something needs to be memorised in place of being understood; or, if understood is too difficult to apply except by rote. Unfortunately, since the procedures for applying compass errors are among the first things taught to navigators, the quite unnecessary rules of thumb are established in the mind at the beginning of a navigator's career and seldom stand a chance of being eradicated because either there seems no necessity to abandon the rules, or the rules seem sufficiently effective to make them justified. This begs the question because not all habits are good ones especially when the habit cannot be recognised as being particularly good or bad. The writer invites the reader to break with tradition by understanding the real meaning of the compass error, its constituent parts, and the significance of each. By so doing some practical advantages may be gained, some misunderstandings and obscurities removed and, perhaps, greater safety ensured.

The Graduated Scale

Essential to the process is to recognise that the compass card is normally an horizontal circular graduated scale pivoted about a vertical axis. Occasionally the plane of the card is either vertical or oblique as in the case of gyro steering repeater presentations. Steering compass presentation may even be in the form of a strip scale. Whatever the type, the 'ship's head' reference is invariably (aboard ship) a lubber's line. Considering the more familiar horizontal scale the most prominent mark is undoubtedly the 'north point'. often graphically adorned and usually designated 000°. The remaining divisions of the scale are marked either clockwise (never anti-clockwise) zero to 359°, or, in the traditional quadrantal notation. The details of marking are very important even though they may seem obvious and known to everyone.

Clockwise and Anti-clockwise Rotation

Having acknowledged the pre-eminence of the north point of the compass the first stage of the rethinking process is to recognise the fact that *East* lies 90° *clockwise* from north and *West* lies 90° *anti-clockwise* from north. Since the card is graduated either continuously clockwise, or quadrantally, it is obvious that in the former case East becomes 090° and West 270°, while in the latter East becomes N90°E and West becomes N90°W. These seeming platitudes are essential to the second stage which is where some even expert authorities appear to confuse themselves as well as others. It is therefore, in the writer's view, most important never to refer either to East lying to the 'right' of north, nor to West lying to the 'left' of north. To introduce the terms *left* and *right* is to obscure and confuse the location of East and West about which there should surely be no doubt whatever in the first place. It is quite mischievous to introduce the left-hand and the right-hand in a subject which deals purely with *rotation*.

Variation

With the entire emphasis upon rotation and excluding all references to 'right' and 'left' the full meaning of variation, deviation and total compass error becomes fundamentally clear. In this sense, if the pre-eminent point of the card (000°), when no deviation exists, settles in a direction *clockwise* from true north then the earth's magnetic field exhibits *Easterly* variation. This is precisely the *meaning* of Easterly variation; likewise, if the north point of the card settles in a direction *anti-clockwise* from true north it *means* the variation is West.

Deviation

Turning to deviation the concept is even more appropriate because of the term used. If the pre-eminent north point of the card is rotated, by the influence of ship magnetic forces, in a direction *clockwise* from magnetic north it, the north point of the card, is *deviated eastward*. Similarly, if it is rotated *anti-clockwise* from magnetic north it is *deviated westward*. This is precisely the fundamental meaning of easterly and westerly *deviation*. Let these statements be compared, for instance, with—'when the direction of compass north lies to the right of magnetic north the deviation is named east—'. Followed immediately by the exhortation, and I quote,— 'this convention should be memorised—'. For what reason should anything be memorised? And what convention is involved except some obscure one caused by the quite unnecessary introduction of the linear directions 'left' and 'right', which are completely irrelevant in this context?

Compass Error

Individual rotations of the compass card from true north, clockwise (easterly) or anti-clockwise (westerly) for variation, and subsequently from magnetic north, clockwise (easterly) or anti-clockwise (westerly) for deviation make up the combined rotation, again clockwise (easterly) and anti-clockwise (westerly) for the total *compass error*.

Provided, therefore, that the navigator recognised the disposition of the directions East and West with respect to North (and south) on the basis of rotation as displayed on a circular compass card, then the correction of courses and bearings from true to compass to set a course, or from compass to true in order to plot bearings on the chart during routine navigation become extremely simple *without any necessity for rules, rhymes and other memory aids*. The important thing to realise is that every individual degree mark on the card is rotated either clockwise or anti-clockwise in sympathy with the rest whenever the compass error is either easterly or westerly respectively. Nothing more need be known.

To Find the Error

To apply these revised conceptions to practical use and to convince the shipboard navigator of their surprising simplicity it is best to consider one or two examples. Suppose, for instance, that an observation is made to ascertain the compass error. A time azimuth is observed and the true bearing of a star found to be 136°(T); the compass bearing at the same instant was 144°(C). How is this possible? Since there is no possible argument for doubting the true bearing of 136°(T) there can only be one explanation; the obvious one, that the compass card has been rotated 8° *anti-clockwise* (Fig. 2), i.e.

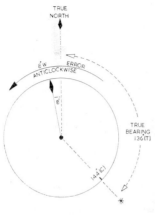

TRUE
NORTH

8° W   ERROR
ANTICLOCKWISE

8°

TRUE
BEARING
136(T)

144(C)

FIG. 2

westerly. The compass error is 8°W. No rules or rhymes are required. It is normal routine at this stage, when recording the facts in the deviation journal, to apply the variation and find the deviation. Suppose, in this instance, that the variation was 10°W. Since the sum of the variation and the deviation totals 8°W the deviation must have been 2°E. This simply records numerically the fact that the compass has been rotated anti-clockwise from true north 10° westward (variation) and subsequently 2° eastward, clockwise (deviation), giving the observed total of 8°W. No rules or rhymes are used.

To Check the Course

It would be natural and necessary at this stage to check the compass course to steer in order to make good the true course between A and B taken from the chart. Suppose the true course is 307°(T). If the compass error is 8°W it is certainly no good steering 307° because the ship would then proceed in a direction 8° to the west (anti-clockwise) of that which was intended! All that is necessary is *mentally* to rotate the card anti-clockwise (westerly) by 8° *against an imagined*

lubber's line. The compass course to steer is 315°(C) (Fig.3).
No rules or rhymes are necessary. Note carefully—variation
and deviation have combined to rotate the card 8°W, thereby
increasing the reading so that 315°(C) corresponds to 307°(T).

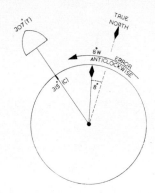

Fig. 3

Correcting Bearings

With the ship proceeding 307°(T) and 315°(C) normal bridge
practice might now require fixes to be obtained by cross bearings
of prominent objects. Three compass bearings are taken and
found to be 041°(C), 172°(C) and 279°(C) (Fig. 4). The
compass error is still 8°W (remember, anti-clockwise). In
order to interpret these compass bearings immediately as true

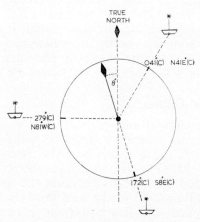

Fig. 4

bearings suitable for plotting on the chart all that needs to be done, *mentally*, is to rotate the compass card 8° *clockwise* from its displaced position, thus removing its error and restoring the north point towards true north.   Each of the observed compass bearings is in consequence reduced by 8° and the true bearings read 033°(T), 164°(T) and 271°(T) (Fig. 5).   No rules or rhymes are required; the true bearings are plotted.   The style of the compass card graduations is immaterial.   Regardless of whether the card is graduated clockwise 000° to 359° or quadrantally from the north and south points towards east and west as shown in Figs 4 and 5, the true bearings are immediately appreciated.   Once the navigator assimilates the basic concepts he will find that he automatically effects the appropriate rotation 'while he takes the bearings' so that the

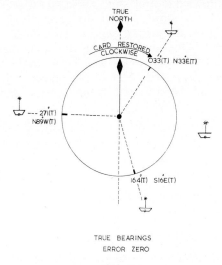

FIG. 5

true bearings are being recorded *directly at the time of observation*; instead of, as is mostly done, the compass bearings are later 'corrected' with the use of a rule or rhyme after reaching the chart table.

No Mistake Possible

In the interests of safety at sea, and assuming that the navigator even at this stage fails to comprehend the simplicity of applying the compass error without resorting to rules and rhymes, there still remains for him the simplest device of all whereby the *compass meridian*, in this case orientated by 8° *anti-clockwise* from the true meridian is drawn directly in pencil on the navigational chart of the area. Compass courses are taken directly from it; compass bearings of distant objects are likewise plotted, and there is no possibility of 'doubling the error' by mistakenly applying it the wrong way! When the course is altered and the error changes the up-dated compass meridian must be redrawn and the original one rubbed out. Again, no rules and no rhymes are required.

Initial Training

At the present time practical navigators are trained technically in much the same manner as they have always been by well-meaning instructors who have themselves acquired their basic knowledge and skill some many years previously. This does not necessarily mean that everything they learned and later pass on is entirely beneficial to those whose turn it is to be taught. One might say that in the matter of compass error appreciation there could well be a wholesale rethinking along the lines suggested. Navigating officer cadets and yacht navigators might be initiated compass-wise with a different approach and be for ever spared the imposition of:—

'Compass to True; add East' Code word CADET
'Compass—East error to Right—True' Code: CERT
'True—East error to Left—Compass' Code: TELC
'True to the Left—Error West'
'Error West—Compass Best'
'Error East—Compass Least,' etc.

Positive and Negative

A *clockwise rotation* (positive) indicates an Easterly error (positive) and naturally supports any rule which applies the error to *compass direction* in order to gain the *true direction*. But since it is equally necessary to reverse the sense of the correction when setting a compass course corresponding to a true course confusion can easily arise. It is this very point which has so unfortunately given rise to the assortment of rules and rhymes and like mnemonics.

The Last Thought

No one would dispute that a rule correctly applied achieves the object but it does so with little or no thought behind it.

Common usage remains its only support. If the reader's traditional inertia, however, can be overcome he may well find the effort worthwhile. He will 'see' in his mind the *real* significance of the compass error, how it is applied in each circumstance, and enjoy the added attraction of knowing confidently what he is doing and why he is doing it.

CHAPTER 3

The Magic Five Degrees.

What are acceptable deviations and why?

ALTHOUGH contemporary use of the gyro compass with its several obvious advantages tends to divert attention from the magnetic compass most navigators are committed to a regular check on the amount of the deviation if for no other reason than the necessity to complete the columns of the deviation journal supplied. Commanding officers however, require this knowledge as prudent navigators because they must anticipate the rare occasions when, through breakdown, they may be deprived of the use of the gyro.

The question which arises at this point is what significance has the sign and amount of deviation beyond the obvious attention it is given when correcting courses and bearings. It is surprising to discover how relatively few junior officers have any real knowledge about deviation other than the necessity for 'applying it' somewhere. It is still more surprising to listen to the reactions of more senior officers.

For instance, given any particular course upon which a deviation of $1\frac{1}{2}°$ or $2°$ has been observed most officers agree that these are tolerable values and cause none of them any concern. This is perfectly reasonable. Given a similar course where the deviation is observed to be $18°$ and the same navigators will instantly react with alarm. They will protest that this is far too much and that the compass should be adjusted as soon as possible, and be equally insistent that it should be done by someone other than themselves.

Questioned further with alternative amounts of deviation, such as $3°$, $7°$, $12°$, $25°$, etc., and the practising navigator, on average comes up with an interesting response which may be partly intuitive, possibly psychological, but rarely rational. *The magic value is $5°$*! Amounts less than this seldom cause concern, while greater values are viewed with suspicion and even fear. Twenty or thirty degrees of deviation are, in the minds of most, quite untenable; they are rarely observed and

14

according to some quite impossible. Although large deviations are unlikely, the writer has experienced 34° of deviation aboard a new ship on its maiden voyage in spite of a proper initial compensation following the acceptance trials. Such values then, are *not* impossible.

Is it Arithmetic?

To return to the unique value of 5°. It seems that, intuitively, values less than this amount are readily accepted simply because they are 'reasonably small' and offer little embarrassment in normal navigational practice. Values over 5° seem to navigators to be unreasonably large or simply, no longer 'small enough'. Of and by itself this is a little strange because once the deviation is known its application is merely a question of arithmetic. Or, can it be that to apply 15° is that much more difficult than to apply 5°? If one considers for a moment the magnetic variation, rather than the deviation, one seldom hears a complaint about its size. It is obtained from the chart and its value never questioned. It may be 3° or 30° and being a geographical feature must be accepted without protest.

Since the compass error is the sum of the variation and deviation, and assuming that the arithmetic involved is the principal case for small deviation, then one might argue that the simplest case would occur when the deviation for the given course was fortuitously equal and opposite to the existing variation. The navigator might cheerfully welcome such a condition because his magnetic compass would be orientated true north/south! Of course, he would be unable to enjoy more than a very few coincidences of this sort.

Directive Force

Questioned more closely about the navigator's preference for deviations which do not largely exceed 5°, very little opinion and constructive thought emerges. Yet, strangely, one does not need to be a compass enthusiast or have a deep knowledge of the subject to provide several most pertinent reasons for preferring a well-adjusted compass featuring very small deviations. Perhaps the most important practical consideration is that if large deviations exist these are accompanied by corresponding differences in the strength of field northward on the several headings.

There is one fundamental truth about compass performance which is ignored all too often—'*If the directing field strength is equal on all headings, no deviation exists.*' The writer reminds the navigator that when deviation is allowed to remain, even in small quantities, then the directive field strength northward changes from heading to heading. It is this, and not the residual deviations, which is anathema to the proper acceptable performance of a magnetic compass. For those who are familiar with the notation of the subject the following examples may be of striking interest; for those unfamiliar the point may still be appreciated by reading between the lines and thereby gaining the significance of the quantities quoted.

Cases in Point

Consider the case of a ship located in European waters where $H = 15$ A/m and $Z = +36$ A/m. The compass is influenced by disturbing field strengths of the order of $P = -4$ A/m, $Q = +1$ A/m and the proportion constants for a, c and e being $-0\cdot10$, $-0\cdot02$ and $-0\cdot25$ respectively.

The deviations on north and south are approximately $4\frac{1}{2}°$ due to Q and no less than $23°$ caused by $P+cZ$ on east and west. The important thing here is the effect on the 'directive force'; the deviation is of secondary consideration. On east and west there are 30% and 17% losses with reference to the ambient earth's field. If it is assumed that a compass of 30 seconds designed period is used then this would be increased to 36 seconds in the one case and 33 seconds in the other by the presence of uncorrected Q together with the effects of a and e.

Allowing for a mean loss of directive force of some 17% caused by a and e it is found that on north, owing to the much larger influence of $P+cZ$, the directive force suffers a loss of no less than 45% with respect to H, while on south there is a temporary gain of 23%. In terms of a 30 seconds period of oscillation these differences extend the period to nearly 40 seconds on north and reduce it to 27 seconds on south. Clearly, the ship cannot confine itself to southerly courses to enjoy the added field strength towards north if, later on, when on northerly courses the existing field strength is nearly halved!

Furthermore, the period of the compass is very important because, except for aperiodic cards, it has been designed to minimise synchronism between it and the roll period. This is most relevant in the event of uncorrected sources of *inclination errors*. The point that is being made here is that by reducing deviation, thereby equalising the northward force over the complete range of headings, the period of oscillation of the compass card is more consistently close to its designed value whichever course the ship pursues. It follows that the instrument functions more steadily upon any course offered and thus reflects the inherent stability of the card originally achieved by Lord Kelvin in 1879.

Altering Course

Apart from the most important effects on 'directive force' the retention of sizeable deviations can embarrass the navigator in a direct sense by misleading him on those occasions when he wishes to alter course through a prescribed arc of the horizon. To do this solely by reference to the compass upon which there are different deviations at the beginning and end of the manoeuvre is to mislead. An alteration of 40° by compass is certainly not 40° 'true' when deviations are allowed to persist.

For example: if the deviation on 000°(C) is zero and on 270°(C) is 10°W then an alteration from 000°(C) to 270°(C) although 90° *by compass* clearly exceeds the fourth part of a circle (the horizon) by 10° and misleads to that extent. This can, of course, be interpreted in the sense that 'degrees by compass' are units of different sizes and bold alterations of course in restricted waters can become navigational hazards, particularly if the deviations are either unknown or are difficult to obtain. For instance, it only needs small amounts of residual quadrantal deviation to provide a real nuisance when it is remembered that only 3° of such uncorrected deviation will deflect the card through 6° when the ship moves from one quadrant to the next because the sign of the deviation changes during the alteration. This is a clear case for a well adjusted compass with only *very small* residual deviations.

It is admitted that large and frequent alterations of course are not normal but the reader may care to speculate upon the war-time procedures of zig-zagging, especially in convoy. A well-adjusted compass was essential (only a minority had gyro compasses) so that large alterations could be made in quick succession without destroying the convoy formation. A further additional case for very small deviations lies in the penalty attached to applying the error incorrectly (it has been done!) whereby the inaccuracy is magnified by a factor of two.

Deviation Curves—Changing the Latitude

Finally, the case for a well-adjusted compass with only the very smallest deviations remaining lies in the changes to be anticipated when a ship covers a considerable range of latitude. This is particularly noticeable when the separate parts of coefficient B have not been properly eliminated by their respective correctors—a condition which most frequently occurs. Except for ships whose voyages are limited to a range of latitudes which does not exceed approximately 30° there should be *no question of the use of a graph or curve of deviation.* Such a curve, or even a list of deviations, appropriate to one latitude can only mislead in another and may cause the ship to pursue a course quite different from that intended. Consider the deviation curves 1 and 2. (Fig. 6.) Curve No. 1 shows the residual deviations at the standard compass in U.K. waters. By the time the ship reached Capetown the deviations at the same compass reached the values shown in Curve No. 2. This was due to the fact that the placing of the Flinders Bar and the fore and aft correctors could not be assured and although the deviations on east and west in U.K. waters did not exceed 2° they concealed values of $5\frac{3}{4}$° and 4° of opposite sign for the two parts of coefficient B. This emphasises that continued reference to a deviation curve for one latitude only serves to confuse in another latitude. In the event steps should have been taken to reduce the observed deviations and one very effective way of doing this lies in eliminating the deviations on east/west courses with fore and aft magnets in low latitudes and adjusting the length of the Flinders Bar in higher latitudes.

It is quite pointless to await the services of a compass adjuster because he has neither the time nor the opportunity to make a detailed study of the behaviour of the deviations over a range of latitude, still less to make an efficient diagnosis of the trouble during the limited time at his disposal aboard.

Asymmetrical Curves

On the subject of deviation curves and their ill-advised use, it is well to point to a very common misconception that all curves 'should' swing approximately equal amounts each side of the mesial line. The only foundation for this popular idea, which is mainly instinctive, is to assume that deviations are necessarily semi-circular; this is quite unjustified and far from the truth.

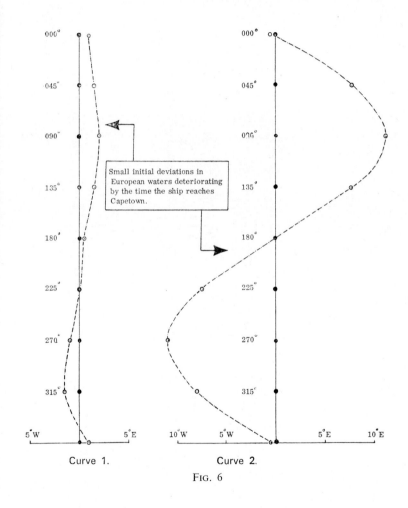

Small initial deviations in European waters deteriorating by the time the ship reaches Capetown.

Curve 1.   Curve 2.

FIG. 6

Consider Curve No. 3 (Fig. 7) which displays a prominent 'bulge' in one single quadrant. This is a very familiar characteristic when there is a small uncompensated amount of quadrantal deviation which becomes cumulative with semi-circular deviation over one sector of the swing.

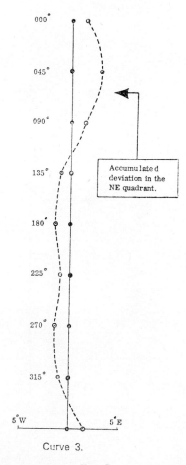

Curve 3.

Fig 7

Safe Navigation

Since the stage has not yet been reached at sea where the magnetic compass can be completely ignored it means that prudent navigators should disregard deviation cards or curves in all but ships navigating within confined limits of latitude. Such curves are worthless and can be very misleading.

It is hoped that practical navigators will cease to attach any significance to the purely arbitrary value of 5° of deviation; it is far too large to be considered 'permissible'. Only the very smallest amounts of deviation are harmless and there is no substitute for a well-adjusted compass with residual deviations near to zero on all headings.

CHAPTER 4

The Fear of the Binnacle - Can it be Overcome?

Adjusting the Compass

'BUT we never do this at sea'—how many times does a navigation instructor hear this remark? If one ranges over the professions there is agreement among instructors, teachers and lecturers that this kind of remark is perennial. Usually the sort of person who makes it is either unsure of himself or a little too sure. If he is a navigator he implies that he has served on every ship afloat and knows what everyone else does. To say the least he presumes too much. To him—'we never do this at sea' only means that he himself has never done it and that he has never seen anyone else do it—whatever it is. Or, is the protester trying to say—'it couldn't be done at sea,' even if one wanted to? Whatever is really meant the younger man is usually blamed for the assertion. And yet, mature and experienced officers also say—'we never do this at sea'. They say it sometimes with greater conviction because of their long and varied experience—experience of what? Never doing it? Never trying to do it? Or not even intending to try doing it? What is it they claim is never done at sea? Why, *to adjust their magnetic compass*, of course.

Obstinacy or Fear?

Whilst never is an absolute term it is certainly true to say that professional navigators (the amateurs are much better at this) very seldom attempt the job and, as they say (to excuse themselves) much prefer to leave it to a professional adjuster! How naive can one get? To adjust a compass is so easy; far easier and much more interesting than so many routine tasks which navigators perform daily. What can a professional adjuster do that the navigator cannot do equally well? Why the traditional inertia, the mystique and even fear which surrounds the prospect of adjustment in the minds of otherwise competent officers? And what of the Master—isn't he often the principal defaulter? Having forgotten what little he knew of the subject he may tend to distrust anyone who has retained a working knowledge, likewise someone who has recently acquired it.

The mystery, the fear and the feeling of—'I don't want to know' which surrounds the binnacle arises from several causes. Perhaps the greatest is simply the lack of urgency or necessity. There seems to be nothing aboard ship which makes it essential that the navigator should remove unwanted deviation. It is not even a habit like taking an eight o'clock sight and running it up to noon—a rather useless exercise of navigation anyway. Cross bearings are taken; compass errors are observed; the radar, echo-sounder and D.F. are all switched on and off as occasion demands, and rightly so; then why not move a magnet or two and get rid of a few degrees of deviation? If complete or even partial adjustment were a habit or a routine it would become second nature, casually accepted and no fuss made about it—in fact one would then say 'everyone does it at sea'.

But there are further reasons why we don't—the most likely is that since the subject was put on the map in 1879 the theoretical extent to which it has been taken has frightened any remaining enthusiasts off it altogether. Most of the details are, or have in fact been, mastered by qualifying officers with no small effort and with some success; but, a few months go by (let alone years) and to most navigators only an uncertain memory remains and a firm conviction 'to have none of it' in practice. The keys of the binnacle are put in the safe, and that's where they remain!

Join the Few

Fortunately however, there is still a minority at sea who have no fears at all over what is really a rewarding part of their professional work when adjusting their magnetic compasses. The writer has little hope of success but he can tempt you to join their small ranks. To try and destroy the senseless taboo which has existed so long. To remove the fear of touching the binnacle and correctors and to remind the navigator that he can hardly make things worse but more likely better, and with so little effort.

What the practising officer aboard ships needs is someone to tell him what can be done easily and usefully and what may be discarded as of purely academic interest in an otherwise practical job of work which has an end-product. The writer, while attempting this, warns that there are some obstinate people about whose stubborness is only equalled by their ignorance. They will, at the outset, offer all the fatuous excuses possible—'I'm not interested; I prefer the gyro'— 'It's all unnecessary; the adjuster can do it'. Such people are tiresome—if you are one of them then don't read any further

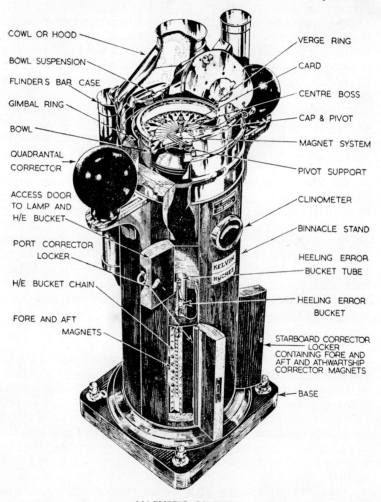

COWL OR HOOD

BOWL SUSPENSION

FLINDERS BAR CASE

GIMBAL RING

BOWL

QUADRANTAL CORRECTOR

ACCESS DOOR TO LAMP AND H/E BUCKET

PORT CORRECTOR LOCKER

H/E BUCKET CHAIN

FORE AND AFT MAGNETS

VERGE RING

CARD

CENTRE BOSS

CAP & PIVOT

MAGNET SYSTEM

PIVOT SUPPORT

CLINOMETER

BINNACLE STAND

HEELING ERROR BUCKET TUBE

HEELING ERROR BUCKET

STARBOARD CORRECTOR LOCKER CONTAINING FORE AND AFT AND ATHWARTSHIP CORRECTOR MAGNETS

BASE

MAGNETIC COMPASS

FIG. 8

Reproduced from 'The Ship's Compass', 2nd Edition, by G.A.A. Grant and J. Klinkert; Routledge & Kegan Paul Ltd.

because we are not on the same wavelength. Apart from the obstinate there are a few who 'know it all'—they needn't read any further either. For the rest, the unprejudiced and by far the majority there is every chance of clearing the decks and being compass-wise to the extent of doing something about it.

Up on the Compass Platform

One can never run before walking. Let the subject of adjustment be temporarily stripped of its official language and technical terms. Let us just eliminate some deviation and let the reasons and the finer points be discussed another time. First thing is to prise the keys of the binnacle from the Master. Convince him somehow that you won't upset anything. Or, if you are the Master, get the keys from the safe; go on the compass platform; open the corrector locker doors and see what's inside. You'll find some fore and aft magnets and some athwartship magnets, probably five or six of each. The former lie lengthwise fore and aft and the latter lengthwise athwartships. Count their number, note which slots they occupy, record whether the red or blue end is visible at the open end of the slot. Then have a rest. Emotionally the most difficult hurdle has been overcome—to open the doors of the corrector lockers. Don't be content with looking at the picture printed in these pages. Look for yourself on the compass platform. Only little children are content with looking at pictures in books. I cannot emphasise more strongly this first step of just *looking*. Many will say that nothing has so far been achieved— that they knew what to expect anyway, so why bother. This is proof that the fear still grips them. Go on—open those locker doors—exorcise the demon and prove something—that you are not scared out of your wits!

Breaking the Ice (Step 1)

Some time or other you will steer a course between 170°(C) and 190°(C). Just mark the occasion especially if the weather is good and the sun is shining. You have a quarter of an hour to spare. Perhaps between 1000 and 1015 hours local ship's time. List the true bearings of the sun at four-minute intervals (four minutes is useful when using azimuth tables) covering the chosen quarter hour. Apply the local variation and record the corresponding magnetic bearings against local time. Let us assume the standard compass course is not many degrees different from 180° with the ship on auto-helm on a

B

corresponding gyro course. The precise course is immaterial. Observe the compass bearing of the sun, for example 106°(C).

Note the difference between this and the magnetic bearing listed for the time by your watch (local ship's time), e.g. 111° (M). The deviation on the present course is clearly 5°E. At this point it doesn't really matter at all whether the deviation is easterly or westerly. The deviation is 5° and it is better to remove it than let it remain.

This can be done in a few moments by noting the assembly of *athwartship* magnets, appreciating the possibility of either raising or lowering one or two of them, or of adding another one to the number already there. With no technical knowledge the navigator will still have no difficulty in removing the deviation by tentatively altering the positions and/or number of the *athwartship corrector magnets.* The deviation will be reduced to zero when the compass and magnetic bearings are made to be the same, namely 111°(M) in this case. Since the auto-helm is steering the ship there is no difficulty in making the steering magnetic compass show the same heading as the standard magnetic compass, in which event the deviation at both compasses has been reduced to zero provided that the lubber lines at both compasses are aligned to the fore and aft line of the ship, a fact which must be accepted at this point. The additional correction at the steering compass requires the help of another officer to monitor the standard compass while the 'adjuster' moves the athwartship magnets at the steering position.

This very simple procedure of removing the deviation on a course near to 180° is one of the easiest and most useful tentative adjustments. There are no complications; the deviation is automatically and simultaneously removed for courses close to 000° and the correction will not deteriorate for some time even after substantial changes of latitude have occurred. *The actual alteration in the position and number of the athwartship magnets should be carefully recorded in the deviation journal with a note of the date, time and geographical position.* Had the ship been pursuing a course close to 000° instead of 180° the process would have been identical. This is merely a matter of circumstance.

Step 2

The entirely painless and extremely simple process of adjusting the athwartship magnets to eliminate the deviation on northerly and southerly courses surprises the navigator who has never done it before to the extent that he wonders why, for so many years, he never tried. Having overcome the inertia once, he is tempted to try again, and the obvious suggests itself—to reduce the deviation on easterly and westerly courses to zero by following the same process as before only on this occasion the magnets to move are those which are positioned lengthwise in the slots which lie parallel to the fore and aft line. These are the *fore and aft magnets*. In all other respects the sequence is identical. A list of magnetic bearings of the sun at small intervals of time is again prepared on a suitable occasion when the weather is fine with the ship on a course within about 10° either side of 090° or 270° One or more fore and aft magnets are raised or lowered so that the compass bearing of the sun is made identical with the magnetic bearing on the prepared list for the appropriate instant of time. In the event the tentative movements of the magnets may be unsuccessful. It may be necessary to introduce an additional magnet. Such spares should be available and possibly found under the chartroom settee!

Having removed the deviation all the relevant details should once more be recorded in the deviation journal. Since we have, in the present context, divested the subject of its official language, it is wise to point out that there are some special circumstances which attend the corrections on easterly and westerly courses. These can be dealt with on a future occasion.

For the moment they do not matter because the navigator is doing substantially the same as any compass adjuster would do in practice.

Step 3

Pursuing this pattern of sighting the deviation and watching it disappear so easily, with so little trouble, and with no more knowledge than that required to work out a time azimuth, it seems only logical to complete the job for what is called the 'upright condition' by likewise reducing to zero any observed deviation which appears whenever the ship pursues a course close to any *one* of the intercardinal headings 045°(C), 135°(C), 225°(C) or 315°(C). Once more the magnetic bearings of the sun are precomputed and listed against local ship's time. The holding down bolts of the sphere correctors are slackened.

With the ship on a course within about 5° of any of the quadrantal headings mentioned the deviation is observed as before. On this occasion the compass and magnetic bearings of the sun for the instant are made identical by moving each sphere corrector a similar amount either towards the compass or further away from it. Movements of approximately half an inch for each sphere should be attempted and both spheres should be moved in the same sense nearer to or further away from the compass. After making these small adjustments the spheres should be disposed symmetrically on each side. Again, a complete record of the event should be entered in the deviation journal.

Some Warnings

Although the simplicity of steps 1, 2 and 3 may be effected at any time as opportunity offers, it would be unwise to assume that this is all there is to compass adjustment. The correction of inclination errors has been omitted at this stage intentionally, as well as some other important details, but this is not to say that there has been an oversimplification. The important points which emerge may be listed.

The Achievement

(i) For the upright condition deviations on all headings are substantially zero, the directive force has been equalised and the compass steadier in consequence.

(ii) The correction will remain valid except for cases where very large changes of latitude are made, in which event the process can be repeated when opportunity offers.

(iii) The experienced gained is invaluable because doing the job instead of talking about it and being afraid of it has convinced the navigator that most of the fears were born of ignorance and were largely imagined. The foundation to a better understanding has been laid; the running is preceded by walking but the walking by sitting down and doing nothing!

'Licking the Compass into Shape'

The sequences which have been detailed should be preserved if possible and while there is some licence over Steps 1 and 2 in so far as they may be done in the reverse order it is important to effect the adjustment of the spheres *last*. There is some opinion, wholly misguided, which suggests an *initial* adjustment of the spheres on any single intercardinal heading. This is most unwise (except in the case of what is called an analysis adjustment), completely wrong in both theory and practice and should never be done. Any attempt at 'licking the compass into shape' by an indiscriminant attack on the deviation is to be deprecatated most strongly.

Those Who Can—Do

There has been no effort to blind the navigator with science; to the contrary. The purpose has been to break the taboos, the fears, and the built-in prejudices which so many officers have when they think of the magnetic compass. The minority who have already tried are the first to confirm the simplicity of doing the job and the satisfaction they have gained by conquering imagined fears that they were incapable. Only the timid will continue to voice their protest. Those who can do, and those who can't or won't will continue to talk most about that of which they know least!

CHAPTER 5

The Last Fears Removed - Confidence in the Compass Restored.

Lack of Safety through Neglect

WE discussed above how the practising navigator could, with a minimum of both knowledge and effort, secure for himself a steady compass with effectively no deviation on all headings with the ship upright. The simplicity of the several operations was emphasised and an attempt was made to remove some of the fears and mystique which have for so long surrounded not just the theory but the practice in the minds of otherwise sane and ordinary folk. The neglect to take some action is, of course, to retain aboard ship magnetic compasses which just plainly cease to function as intended—to point steadily in a magnetic north direction. The facts may be ignored (too often are) in which case all is well until there is a gyro failure. Then the navigator uses an apparently deficient compass, blames its shortcomings, abuses it without justification and impairs the safety of the ship accordingly. Clearly, further action is necessary.

Rolling in a Seaway

Probably the most outstanding cause of poor magnetic compass performance is the neglect to up-date the correction of inclination errors or, simply, heeling error. When the ship is set on a course within a few degrees of 000° or 180° and is rolling in a seaway the odds are considerable that both the standard and steering (if fitted) magnetic compasses are swinging to and fro in some cases upwards of 10° to 15° either side of the lubber's line. This is not to say that the ship's head is swinging even though one recognises the tendency to yaw, particularly with a quarter sea and swell; rather that the compass displays little sign of indicating the instantaneous direction of the ship's head. Navigators have a happy knack of either not noticing this erratic behaviour, or, if they have, carefully avoiding doing anything about it. Yet, the remedy is extremely simple if done on a tentative basis and literally takes only a few moments—moments, not minutes. Under the conditions of heading near to north or south, with the ship rolling, the heeling error magnet bucket chain should be located within the corrector locker and gently pulled to raise the bucket with whatever corrector magnets it contains. This action will have either the effect of making the compass much steadier, or it will swing even more wildly than before. Even the uninitiated cannot fail to sense if he is on the right track. If there is a noticeable improvement then the bucket should be raised still further and/or additional magnets added to those existing and inserted with the same colour uppermost. If the compass performance deteriorates the bucket should be lowered, the number of magnets reduced, reversed if necessary and added to until the compass is completely steady. The whole operation is very rewarding because the officer who attempts it need know nothing of the theory of inclination errors and their cause to turn an unsteady and useless compass into a steadily-pointing instrument.

One Latitude Only

Having, by these simple means, made the standard and steering magnetic compasses steady under rolling conditions it must be remembered that this improvement will only be maintained if the ship does not substantially change her latitude. The further the ship departs to a higher or lower latitude the less effective will be the tentative correction until renewed oscillations appear and the process must be repeated. Officers who have studied the subject will know (if they have not forgotten) that the correction is appropriate to only one latitude because the type of corrector used (magnets placed vertically) is strictly incompatible with the group of forces it is trying to eliminate. The burden of repeated correction along the lines suggested must therefore be accepted while the system of correction remains unchanged. But this is no hardship because it is so easy to do, takes so little time, and bears the reward of always having a steady compass to steer by if the need arises. It follows that bridge officers need to lose no opportunity of repeating this correction as often as it is required. Any tendency, having gone through the routine, to accept the correction as permanent simply defeats the object; it might as well have been left alone in the first place. Habitual checking and readjustment is the only answer. If possible it should precede the normal adjustments for the 'upright' condition but the sequence may be violated occasionally on the basis that it is better to secure a steady compass in a seaway than to await the ideal conditions for a more formal approach and have to put up with a useless compass in the meantime!

Objections to Seagoing Adjustment

It seems that having spelt out in simple words the means by which navigating officers can secure an efficient magnetic compass against the possibility of a gyro breakdown there still remains the need to overcome two possible objections. The first is that odd habit of retaining a careful record of deviations,

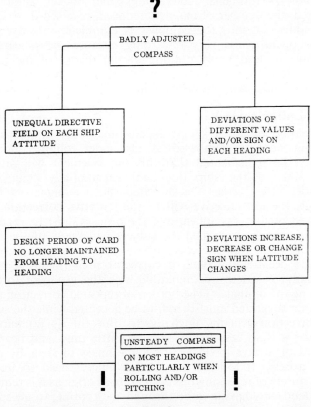

FIG. 9

and to use these deviations in appropriate areas whenever the sky is clouded and error checks are unobtainable. This is considered by some to be preferable to removing the deviation by adjustment.   What a curious philosophy this is—to want to preserve the deviation when the essence is to get rid of it! The master who knows that he is working with a well-adjusted compass has no need to worry about the deviation which he has been at pains to eliminate.   It no longer exists.   What is the point of trying to make something out of nothing!   In such cases the entries in the journal simply confirm, watch by watch, that only fractional amounts of deviation remain.   Why is the nature of the beast so perverse then?   Simply, that it is easier to retain the deviation, as if it was something precious, than to display the courage required to destroy it.   No case whatever can be made for such weakness.

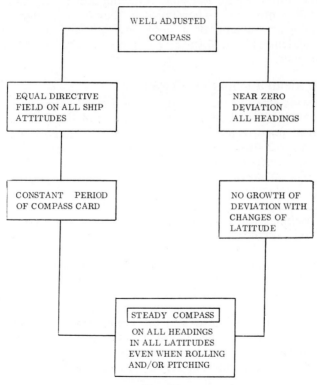

FIG. 10

The second point, which sounds so much like another excuse to dodge the issue, is that in the event of a stranding and a subsequent inquiry blame of some kind may be attached to ships' officers who have performed their own adjustments instead of employing the services of a professional adjuster. This has no foundation in fact. No one need dispense with the professional expert when he is available. Shipboard adjustment at sea is additional to and follows naturally the formal swings carried out in the precincts of a port. For over 100 years the Marine Ministries and Departments have actively ensured, or tried to ensure, that qualifying navigating officers should have a thorough knowledge of both the theory and practice of the subject. Why should they display this concern if they did not intend that it should be implemented? There should be no confusion over these points; both masters and senior officers cannot beg the question of having satisfactory and well-adjusted compasses. The choice is theirs; an unsteady and unreliable instrument, or a stable and efficient one—little or no confidence in the former—complete reliance in the latter. It's as plain as that.

More about Inclination Errors

Having stressed the importance of a steady compass in the pursuit of safe and efficient navigation, and the fact that the causes of uncorrected inclination errors contribute more than anything else to unsteadiness, it is necessary to mention that the uncorrected forces which produce unsteadiness when the ship rolls on northerly and southerly courses are the same or similar forces which create unsteadiness on easterly and westerly courses when the ship pitches. Usually the former are referred to as heeling error forces and the latter as pitching error forces. The navigator needs to be reminded that, provided the causes of *quadrantal deviation* have been previously removed by the proper placing of the soft iron spheres (correcting co-efficient D) then, the proper adjustment of the vertical magnets referred to above will secure the elimination of unsteadiness due to both *rolling and/or pitching* in a seaway. In other words two birds are killed with one stone and the entire group of disturbing forces which produce inclination errors in general are removed. But, we must repeat, this can only happen if the quadrantal correctors (spheres) have been previously properly adjusted. In the event of this detail not having been carefully attended to the shipboard adjuster has the choice of adjusting the vertical magnets to eliminate either the unsteadiness on north/south courses due to rolling, or on east/west courses due to pitching, but not both. The obvious choice is the former because unsteadiness due to rolling always predominates, simply because ships roll more than they pitch.

Further Penalties of Unsteadiness

It is hoped that the reader has been encouraged to discriminate between a steady compass working efficiently and one that oscillates in a manner which practically precludes its use for the proper purpose. It is hoped also, that some attempt will be made to achieve the former by following some or all of the suggestions made in this and the previous chapter. Failure by omission has only one consequence—confidence in the use of the magnetic compass is lost. If the magnetic compass is of the transmitting type, and many ships are fitted with these, it simply means that every part of the ancillary equipment which is monitored by the compass suffers in sympathy. The autohelm becomes useless through over-work, the stabilised radar picture is no longer stabilised, the D.F. likewise. One can only make the point that without subsequent concern for and positive action taken in the matter of adjustment a transmitting magnet compass is wasted money and were best not fitted in the first place.

The writer wishes to add, to encourage others, that officers who have tried tentative adjustments along the lines suggested are the first to acknowledge the simplicity of the exercise. They are likewise enthused with the results, gain enormous confidence, and look upon those who will not try as out of their tiny minds. For these the prospect of meandering across the oceans in the vague and general desired direction is the most that can be hoped for. All the closed loops will be working overtime and the meaning of 'steady as she goes' will remain a mere paradox.

CHAPTER 6

The Separation of B in Practice.

The means by which the navigator aboard might overcome his fears of the binnacle and acquire a steady compass to steer by in the event of a gyro breakdown have been suggested in previous sections. Some licence has been taken for the sake not only of simplicity but to encourage action. In the interests of safe navigation and to appease those who feel their wider knowledge of compass work has not been justified it is time to look further and to direct attention, in this instance, to the separation and correction of the two parts of coefficient B.

Square One

THERE is not a qualified master mariner to whom the phrase 'splitting B' does not remind him of the classroom and countless variations on a theme of coefficient B. Theoretically, and often in make-belief, he wrestled with the disposition of the Flinders bar and fore and aft corrector magnets. He wandered over the oceans from one hemisphere to the other, solved endless problems, achieved the right answers and ultimately returned to the bridge and wondered what it was all about.

Can there be a topic where so much has been learned by so many and put to such little use? Colleges of navigation, examination centres, instructors and qualifying officers have had endless years of fun 'splitting B'. But on the bridge only a handful of professionals have ever shipped a length of Flinders bar or know what it looks like. In fact, faced with finding out how much of the stuff exists for'd of the compass, most officers tend to remove the brass cap, sight the end of the corrector, attempt to remove it, give up, and replace the cap without ever knowing that the whole tube (paint permitting) can be withdrawn.

Some facts about the deviations appearing on 090°/270° constitute square one in the subsequent procedure of reducing them to zero. If it is assumed that the compass is well placed (on the fore and aft centre-line) the approximate co-efficients A and E are either negligible or zero so that only coefficient B need be considered. In the notation of the subject Sin $B°$ $= (P+cZ)/\lambda H$ using λH as a mean value of the directing field northward. Provided that the deviation is not excessive $B° = 57.3 (P+cZ)/\lambda H$. It follows that the observed deviations on 090°/270° are caused in part by the forward component of the low permeability magnetisation of the ship (P) acquired when building and the remainder by the forward component of the high permeability magnetisation of the ship's structure (cZ) perpendicular to the deck. Thus the total observed deviation on east/west courses is popularly known as coefficient total B and its constituents as coefficients permanent and induced B.

The Adjuster's Problem

Although it is fashionable to place the onus of proper adjustment upon the professional adjuster it is quite unfair to put the full responsibility of the separation and correction of coefficient B upon his shoulders when it is beyond his power to do more than effect a tentative approach.

There are only three alternatives open to the adjuster operating in the precincts of a port. He may correct entirely with fore and aft permanent magnets (easy), entirely with the Flinders bar (awkward), or he may use any of a large number of combinations of the two (usual).

In each case he has no difficulty eliminating the deviation but this only means that the inaccuracy of the individual compensations for the two parts of coefficient B creates problems in other latitudes for which he cannot be held responsible because he has no further alternative.

This places the burden of adjusting each corrector to fulfil its designed purpose fairly and squarely with the navigators aboard ship. But this is a platitude because everyone who has studied the subject knows it—and then proceeds to do nothing about it!

Frequently, and with more ships than ever rounding the Cape, large deviations (often more than 20°) are found on east/west courses, the compass pronounced as useless, the Saints blessed because there is a gyro aboard, and the adjuster exhorted 'to do something with the Flinders bar' to prevent it happening again. In these circumstances the adjuster might be forgiven for losing patience because he is seldom, if ever, provided with the precise information necessary to solve the problem completely. The most he can hope for is the deviation journal with its bleak evidence of what happened on previous voyages. He has little time and opportunity to make proper calculations when everyone is waiting for him to finish the swing, discharge both himself and the pilot and ring 'full away' on the next passage. In the event the professional will tentatively alter the length of the Flinders bar in the light of the amount existing and the size and sign of the growth of deviation in some remote latitude as reported.

Often these inspired estimates pay off and when the ship returns the navigators are full of praise. Meanwhile the professional, pleased with the fortuitous result, wonders why those aboard couldn't have helped themselves with both the time and means available to do the job properly.

There can be no doubt that in practice the neglect and failure are acts of omission. The examining authorities for the statutory qualifications of deck officers have, for upwards of a century, required a theoretical proficiency and can hardly be blamed for such omissions on the bridge. Navigators, well aware of the problem frequently say, 'it's too difficult', and therefore 'we'll not bother.' Others, that 'we're afraid to touch the thing,' which is probably true.

Always, some excuse is offered for dodging the issue and when there are no more excuses the subject is dismissed as being 'not worth bothering about, because we have the gyro,' and so on. Until the gyro breaks down and the problem obtrudes again. Better, surely, to face the fact of ignorance or forgetfulness and seek the remedies.

The Magnetic Equator

The problem of separating the two parts of coefficient B by itself has, as most people know who have studied the subject, only two methods of solution. The first and most obvious is to take advantage of the unique conditions which obtain if and when the ship crosses or approaches the *magnetic equator*. In these areas the earth's vertical component of force (Z) is either negligible or zero, cZ in consequence substantially zero and the deviation appearing on 090°/270° caused solely by P. *If this is eliminated by adjusting the fore and aft corrector magnets deviation cannot subsequently appear due to P.* It follows that any future deviations which appear on 090°/270°, once the ship departs from the vicinity of the magnetic equator, are caused by cZ and should be eliminated by altering the length of the Flinders bar.

Most navigators, who have at some time studied the subject, are well aware of this simple procedure. Since fear usually predominates, the first essential to effect the necessary adjustments is the courage to do them. The second prerequisite is obviously the fact that the intended voyage includes either the close approach to, or the actual crossing of the magnetic equator; if neither are likely no more need be said of the method. This immediately raises the question of identifying the magnetic equator and knowing when the ship reaches it. Admiralty charts Nos. 5383 (dip) and 5378 (Z) both delineate the magnetic equator and are essential to any further action. Unfortunately, the folio containing miscellaneous charts aboard ship does not always include these rather special charts. The omission should be rectified and the chart equipment brought up to standard. Again, there should be no excuses such as— 'We don't carry these charts,' or—'They are not supplied in our Company', or, simply—'I've never seen these charts'! The answer is to indent for them at the first opportunity.

When the Magnetic Equator is Not Reached

In the event of voyages which do not extend to the magnetic equator the obvious advantages of doing so cannot be enjoyed. The proper separation of the two parts of coefficient B is then more lengthy; consists of observing the deviations on 090°/270° in two widely-separated latitudes; forming two equations involving the two unknown parts equated to the observed coefficient in each location, and solving the equations from which the separate parts caused by P and cZ are found. In such cases Admiralty chart No. 5379 (H) is desirable in addition to those already mentioned.

The details of the computations required need not be explained here; those who have experienced them know what is involved and those who haven't needn't worry about them because some practical alternatives are submitted below which make the strictly quantitative approach secondary to the removal of unwanted deviation. Nevertheless, some aspects of the 'splitting B' problem should be considered at this stage to indicate what is useful and what may be considered superfluous in practice.

If one bears in mind the purpose of the exercise, which is to remove deviation on 090°/270° with the appropriate combination of Flinders bar and magnet, then only one really useful calculation exists. The conditions to which it applies are listed as follows:—

(i) The observed deviations on 090°/270° are known in a given geographic locality for which Z and H are obtained from the charts.

(ii) An arbitrary assumed amount of the coefficient is taken and attributed to cZ (coefficient induced B) and then eliminated with an appropriate length of Flinders bar suitably placed.

(iii) The *remaining deviation* which, as a result of (ii) above, may be more or less than that originally observed is then likewise removed with fore and aft horizontal magnets.

(iv) The observed coefficient is then determined in a second geographic location where Z and H have appreciably changed as shown on the charts.

(v) The calculation is now effected in favour of the two parts of the observed coefficient (iv, above), each found, and the two correctors adjusted on the binnacle to produce zero deviation as intended.

In subsequent latitudes near zero deviations will occur because each part of the total coefficient has been properly catered for by its intended corrector. Such a calculation is valid and constructive because it deals with and solves a real-life situation. In practice the shipboard operator may simplify and achieve the same result by ignoring the assumed quantities in (ii) above. This is reasonable because the need only arises to determine the significance of the deviation which *appears in the second position*, (iv) above. It is *only necessary to calculate the measure of over or undercompensation* on the part of each corrector. Once these are known they can be adjusted without the need to know the actual value of each part of the total coefficient which belongs to the ship. After all, the deviation appearing at the second location only arises on account of the inevitable over or undercompensation which has to be rectified. This is simply another way of saying that the manner of dealing with the original coefficient, (ii) above, is of no importance in practice because in every case it is reduced to zero by one means or another. In this connection the writer has seen many academic problems in which, for some curious and unexplained reason, it is required to determine the two parts of the total coefficient at the *starting position*! The purpose of this is difficult to understand particularly when one remembers that they cannot be found without first visiting some other geographic location. Even when the original parts are determined; of what practical use is this knowledge when it is too late? One has to guard against calculating for the sake of it and of looking a bit foolish in the process. Of course, as mentioned earlier, the variations on a theme of coefficient B are endless; many problems are set in examinations which hardly relate to practice, are nevertheless interesting on their own account but serve little useful purpose. The writer apologises to qualifying officers on whom he has, through circumstances, had to inflict a few unrealistic problems of this sort. A case in point concerns the observed deviations on 090°/270° in two widely-separated latitudes followed by a calculated or graphed estimate of the amount likely to appear in a third or fourth location. Why should this concern the navigator when, if he knows his job, the correctors should have been adjusted at the second location with the express intention of ensuring a well-adjusted compass over the whole subsequent range of latitude! ? What is the point of measuring the deterioration when all the steps have been taken and the means are available to avoid it?

Coefficient B Uncorrected

Before looking at the alternatives available for eliminating the deviation on 090°/270° aboard ship it is worth examining a possible case on a voyage bound from London to Mombasa via the Cape and return to Liverpool. The observed coefficient at London was +5°. If, in fact, this was composed of −7° caused by the induced part of the coefficient (cZ) and the remaining +12° by the permanent part (P), the forecast of the total deviation which appears off each port during the voyage would be as shown (Fig. 11), provided no steps were taken to eliminate it. Little change develops at the beginning and end of the voyage but large *changes* (and large deviations) occur when the ship penetrates the southern hemisphere. In the case shown this is largely due to the induced part of coefficient B reversing its sign on the approach to Capetown. The two parts tend to be cumulative rather than cancel each other. Clearly, the case for correction is overwhelming but the adjuster at London cannot know which of an infinite number of arrangements of Flinders bar and magnet is the correct combination. Suppose, and that's all one can do, that a

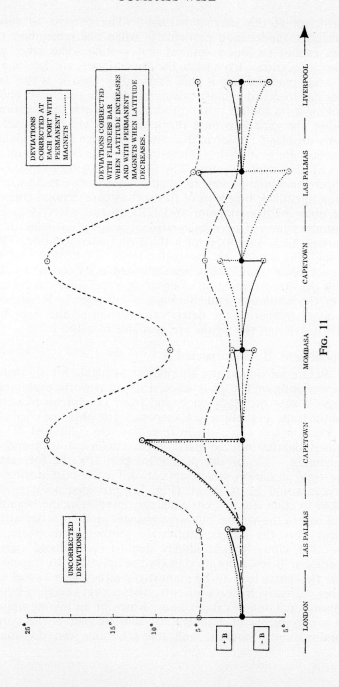

DEVIATIONS
CORRECTED AT
EACH PORT WITH
PERMANENT
MAGNETS   ....

DEVIATIONS CORRECTED
WITH FLINDERS BAR
WHEN LATITUDE INCREASES
AND WITH PERMANENT
MAGNETS WHEN LATITUDE
DECREASES.

UNCORRECTED
DEVIATIONS ----

Fig. 11

length of Flinders bar was shipped to increase the observed deviation ($+5°$) to $+10°$ and the remainder ($+10°$) was eliminated with fore and aft magnets. The curve of residual coefficient B appears as shown by the dash-dot curve provided again that the correctors remain untouched during the round voyage. These estimates at London were fortuitously accurate, each corrector under-compensating initially by only $2°$ so that no deviation in excess of $5°$ occurred during the round trip. But this was pure luck and might well have turned out otherwise. At this point the reader will recognise that the graph, while apparently encouraging, might well have displayed a still smaller amplitude, or a *much larger one*, depending upon the combination of the two correctors placed initially. Chance alone decides the ultimate success together with an inspired guess that most ships exhibit a negative cZ in the northern hemisphere which is why the Flinders bar case invariably appears as a more or less permanent fixture on the fore side of the binnacle.

Coefficient B Corrected with Fore and Aft Magnets

Owing to the uncertainty with which coefficient B is corrected initially no great harm attaches to dispensing with the Flinders bar and using the magnets alone. In this event small deviations are maintained *provided that the magnets are readjusted to eliminate deviation whenever opportunity offers on* $090°/270°$ *courses*. The graph shows the likely sequence if the deviation appearing off each port is removed. This is not, it is emphasised, a plea to dispense with the Flinders bar altogether but it is an obvious method of ensuring negligible deviation if one has not the means of using the Flinders bar properly. It is a cause for action as opposed to inaction.

Coefficient B Corrected in the Kelvin Tradition

In case conscience-stricken navigators feel that the sole use of the magnets suggested above, offends against the proprieties to the extent that they feel uncomfortable about it there remains what is probably the most practical method of all. Attributed to Lord Kelvin, the method recommends that the deviations on $090°/270°$ courses should be reduced to zero with fore and aft *magnets* whenever the ship moves to a *lower latitude*, while the length of the *Flinders bar* should be altered to eliminate the deviation on those occasions when the ship *increases latitude*. The concept is both sensible and practical.

It rightly assumes a steady growth of deviation caused by cZ in the higher latitudes and a corresponding decrease in lower latitudes. It recognises which part of coefficient B predominates over the range of latitude and points to the more appropriate corrector at any stage of the voyage. The graph shows, in the present case, the likely effect of successive adjustments along these lines. After the return voyage the deviation is less than 2° and will remain so because the two parts of the coefficient are now substantially corrected by the proper combination of Flinders bar and magnet. No calculations are required and very little knowledge. Of course, the special case of the magnetic equator, q.v., simplifies the scheme and shortens the process considerably as might be expected.

This very attractive tentative approach was suggested towards the close of the last century; it is odd that it has so seldom been adopted, and for those officers aboard ship who dislike the prospect of computing and solving equations it seems that the advantages of such a tentative approach should be more than welcome. One might hope, in the cause of general safety, that instead of proclaiming with some perverse satisfaction that large deviations appeared rounding the Cape or crossing the Australian Bight, that only very small deviations on 090°/270° courses were in fact achieved by the method suggested.

Home Coast Procedure

There remains a final alternative procedure for correcting coefficient B on ships whose voyages do not extend beyond certain reasonable limits of latitude. In such cases both parts of the coefficient may be eliminated with *fore and aft magnets* and the Flinders bar dispensed with. Furthermore, apart from obvious long-term readjustments, the magnets need not be touched from one voyage to the next. This process is sometimes referred to as a 'home coast procedure' on the basis that voyages are unlikely to cover a wide range of latitude. Whilst this is acceptable within limits it is often overlooked that many voyages extend over a wide range of longitude without large changes of latitude. In this sense the 'home coast procedure' need not exclude foreign voyages. In fact there are many foreign voyages where the range of latitudes covered is far less than that which embraces the 'home coast'!

Since only permanent corrector magnets are used it follows that, in all but the latitude in which the initial correction was done, deviations will appear on 090°/270° courses. It remains to define the size of deviations which may be tolerated during such a process. This cannot be done absolutely for the simple reason that, as in all cases, the separate parts of coefficient B remain unknown throughout. What can be done, however, is to consider the high permeability part of the coefficient (deviation caused by cZ) and decide what proportion of this might be accepted throughout the voyage/s as a small deviation. It must be remembered that deviation, if known, can be applied and causes little bother provided that it is small. The important thing is that in cloudy areas it may be impossible to check; it is then reassuring to create conditions where the amount of deviation is unlikely to exceed a certain value even though it remains unknown. Such is the purpose of the 'home coast procedure'.

The method clearly demands a starting position, or that location in which the initial correction is effected. In the following example London is chosen where $H = 0.184$ and $Z = +0.450$ oersteds respectively. The field strengths are not expressed in S.I. units in this instance because charts showing them are not yet available. If it is assumed that the deviations to be considered are not excessive then they may be taken as proportional to the component forces causing them. Let y represent the conjectured amount of the induced coefficient at London and δ the deviation to be expected on arrival at some other position for which H_2 and Z_2 are the appropriate elements. Under these conditions,

$$\delta = \frac{H_1}{H_2}\left(\frac{Z_2}{Z_1} - 1\right) y$$

The tolerated proportion is then,

$$\frac{\delta}{y} = \frac{H_1}{H_2}\left(\frac{Z_2}{Z_1} - 1\right) = \frac{0.184}{H_2}\left(\frac{Z_2}{0.45} - 1\right)$$

Assuming that δ/y should not exceed, say, 10%

$$0.1\,H_2 = 0.41\,Z_2 - 0.184 \quad \dots \quad \text{(i)}$$

If $0.35\,\text{Cos}\lambda$ is written for H and $0.70\,\text{Sin}\lambda$ for Z, where λ is the magnetic latitude we have,

$$\text{Sin}\lambda = 0.1219\,\text{Cos}\lambda + 0.6411$$

Substituting $\sqrt{1 - \text{Cos}^2\lambda}$ for Sinλ the following quadratic equation is evolved,

$$\text{Cos}^2\lambda + 0.154\,\text{Cos}\lambda - 0.580 = 0 \quad \dots \quad \text{(ii)}$$

From which $\lambda = 46° 28'$ N. Since the magnetic equator is located some 10° north of the geographical equator on the meridian of Greenwich this places an upper limit to the latitude beyond which deviations greater than 10% of the original induced B would occur. In this case the latitude is $56\frac{1}{2}°$N approximately. The sign of the deviation appearing will be the same as that of the original induced B except in cases where the local bridge structure has reversed the sign from normal. In the event the actual sign is not significant because the Flinders bar is not used and has therefore no cause to be secured aft of the compass. The lower limit of latitude naturally invokes a change of sign in the deviation and can be calculated, in this instance, by substituting $-0\cdot1$ for $+0\cdot1$ in equation (i) above. Other limits, say for 20% ($\pm$ 0·2) can be calculated in a similar way.

Limits of Voyages

Figure 12 indicates the extent of voyages based on London, where the deviations appearing are no more than 10% and 20% of the original induced B. Even though London is located in a high-dip area ($+69°$) the induced coefficient B would seldom exceed 15° and would more often be little more than 10°. Within the 10% area deviations of less than 1° will appear and in the 20% area little more than 2°. Even allowing for excessive values the deviations will always be less than, say, 3°. The trend of the isoclinic lines in the North Atlantic closely approximates that of the magnetic equator. The reader will no doubt quickly appreciate that this is fortuitous for voyages to the east coast of U.S.A. and, if the 20% limits are accepted, to practically the whole of the Mediterranean as well, with the Gulf of Mexico as an added bonus.

Although the 'home coast procedure' is recommended for small ships (less than 60 metres in length) by the Department of Trade (M. Notice 616/72) it is clear that the method can be used with discretion on foreign voyages as well. The method can be used on ships of all sizes; it is not clear why small ships should be so favoured and larger ships excluded from the recommendation. Any place in the world can be used as a datum position and similar limits defined for values acceptable to the navigator.

The End Product

As is always the case, the balance between theory and practice should be preserved. It is of little avail to master the theory of separating coefficient B and then do nothing about it.

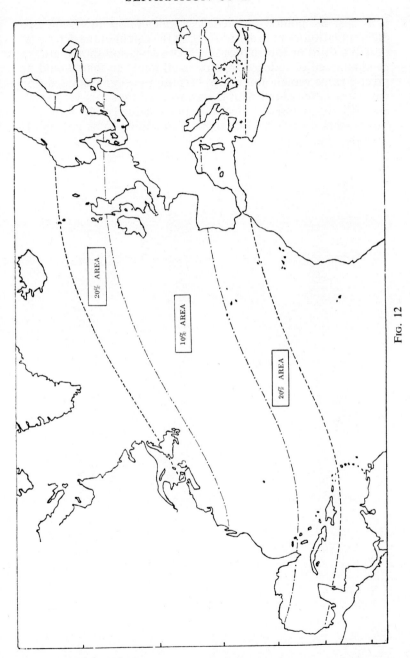

20% AREA

10% AREA

20% AREA

Fig. 12

It is just as pointless to effect a calculation involving two different latitudes in order to forecast the extent of the deterioration in a third or fourth location. The deviation should always be eliminated or reduced to very small limits so that should its precise value remain unknown, because the sky is clouded, the navigator is reassured with the knowledge that it is very small and will not materially affect the course made good. After all, this is what deviation is all about—something to be got rid of! It's safer that way.

CHAPTER 7

The Deviation Journal - Some Rethinking.

The officer of the watch might care to reflect upon that which he does every time he's on the bridge and scarcely thinks about. Probably one of the first things an officer cadet has to do aboard ship, on the bridge, as an act of practical navigation, is to 'take an error'. Subsequently, as an officer he performs this ritual with unfailing regularity and faithfully records every occasion in the Deviation Journal. It is so familiar and such an apparently insignificant part of his duties that it hardly warrants a second thought; and yet, the reader is invited to ponder the process, gain a few ideas, reorientate his thinking along more realistic lines and, it is hoped, come out feeling better for the experience.

Why Think About It?

Perhaps every habit, good and bad, suffers from the fact that it is essentially automatic, an act of repetition, and therefore gains little thought in the process of execution. Sometimes routine performances, generated as good habits, become, if not bad habits, at least routines over which many of the reasons for doing them become obscured. The navigator can easily fall into the trap when he 'takes an error', and is asked 'why'? He says, 'well, everybody takes errors'—'You must take an error, or how would you know what it was'. This is the natural reaction, the obvious answer which might normally close the subject. But not on this occasion, it isn't! Taking compass errors can become like animals performing tricks at a circus. They don't know quite what they are doing and only vaguely why they are doing it; they hardly enjoy it because they don't have to think about it. To all of which the reader may seriously wonder where the glamour can possibly arise from such an ordinary and uninspiring chore. Let us think a little more about this. Circus animals don't have to think, poor devils—we are supposed to think of why, and when, and how—let us do this.

49

Why, When and How?

In Chapter 16 the writer mentions the several faults which can arise when aligning gyro repeaters with the master compass and touches upon some of the bridge practices when ascertaining the compass error and deviation at the standard magnetic compass. It appears that these routines are often even worse than was suggested, and for the most astonishing reasons.

Why are errors taken at all? Firstly, as everyone knows, to establish the deviation at the standard compass and to ensure that it is either very small or zero. If it turns out to be at all sizeable the compass efficiency is impaired because the field strength northward is uneven on the several headings. Notice the order of priority here. The *standard magnetic compass* is assumed to be the *standard datum* for heading reference *in case there is a gyro failure*. Nevertheless, most navigators put the magnetic compass in second place of importance—surely this would only be justified on those few ships carrying two independent gyro compasses? From the number of gyro failures, including power failures, which are reported, there is still a very strong case for the magnetic compass to be the first priority compass, in which case the knowledge of the error and the deviation is essential to making the intended course and to practise the normal routines of navigation along the leg of each traverse. Assuming the standard magnetic compass in the position of first priority as a heading reference the next question is 'when'?

Normal custom dictates that errors should be taken each watch and this appears still to be traditional, and so the habit persists. The master's standing orders seldom indicate that errors should be taken specifically on the standard compass; the likely directive is simply that compasses and courses should be verified by the two officers exchanging watches. Usually there is no reference to any particular compass and the matter is left to the discretion of individual officers. Since it is less trouble and more convenient they, in turn, choose the gyro as the standard reference. The fact that the gyro assumes first priority has, therefore, in these days, encouraged navigators to waive the necessity for taking an error soon after altering course. On many ships when altering course the same small gyro error is assumed without further thought. Surely, substantial changes of course are only likely during coastal navigation, i.e. in an area where the heading reference should be under *guarantee* in the event of a gyro breakdown. Does this not indicate the obvious necessity for checking the magnetic compass *very soon* after each alteration of course?

If deviation is present: does this not change with heading? Isn't it better to know what it is? If the gyro *does* break down in a congested area; don't you want to know the compass course to steer *when you need it most*? Or, is one to be content with a complete shambles at a time when everything should be under control?

But 'when' and 'how' are closely connected. The gyro is too convenient (when everything is working fine) that not many bother very much after altering course. The casual practice of noting the difference between the steering repeater and the standard compass periscope heading is the most that is done. Why? Because it is inconvenient to walk outside and take another error? Is it that the well-appointed and no doubt air-conditioned wheelhouse is too comfortable to leave except once a watch to take an error, and then only as far as the wing repeater?

Perhaps it needs a very single-minded professional, in the best physical condition, to get as far as the compass platform to take an error at the standard compass! Do such as these encourage junior officers to do the same? Where does the fault lie—with the juniors alone—or, have the seasoned officers changed good habits for bad ones—'because everybody does it'?

The trouble with this casualness lies solely in the matter of *compass comparisons*. Often the error is taken on any nearby bearing repeater which means that the *compass bearing* was taken on the repeater, *assumed* to be the same on the steering repeater, heading reference then made with the standard compass periscope and the *supposed* compass bearing interpreted for the standard compass as a result! No less than three uncertain heading references! Could there be a more tortuous procedure? Were the repeaters aligned accurately from the start? Two out of the three lubber lines may be in error, or slightly displaced. Why shouldn't they be—have you checked them? All this has been pointed out in these pages before— the whole process is fraught with inconsistencies. The writer makes no apology for repeating yet again that there is only one way to find the error and deviation at the standard compass— *by taking the compass bearing at the standard compass itself*. This quite dangerous and unseamanlike process of comparing headings is to be deplored, especially if it is used to obtain a compass bearing on a compass to which the navigator never even went near! How tired can you get? A bearing is a bearing, which means taking it with an azimuth mirror—lubber lines and heading references should have nothing whatever to do with *bearings*. To make matters still worse the error and deviation at the standard compass is made yet more uncertain by officers of the watch occasionally using the port wing repeater and at other times using the starboard wing repeater, the sole criterion being the direction from which the wind is blowing and making sure of enjoying the comfort of the lee side. The fact that a further heading reference is invoked to upset the accuracy of the end product just hasn't crossed the mind. This kind of thing is just sheer madness—but it's what goes on just the same.*

*A professional adjuster's recent report: a periscopic compass leaking at deck joint. Repaired and replaced. Lubber line displaced 6° to starboard. Time not available for complete resiting.

Never Let it be Said

The deviation journal, more about which in a moment, often contains entries by navigating officer cadets. This is good and should be encouraged but the most junior officers and cadets must guard against the worst crime of all. Let us explain this with some delicacy. The journal is familiar to all—successive entries, one following the other, often for the same or a similar course.

The errors and deviations correspond closely. A junior officer occasionally takes an error, computes the true bearing, ascertains the error and deviation only to find that each disagrees with those recorded by previous watch-keepers. It is not unknown in such a case, for the bearings to be conveniently trimmed here and there and the cooked ingredients made to produce a more acceptable result agreeing more closely with others already recorded. This deceit is sometimes indulged in for the understandable reason that the person who does it is disinclined to demonstrate any ineptitude or inaccuracy to his seniors. The record is then made to appear all right. There is here no intention of offending those who are stepping on to the ladder, or those who have ascended the lowest rungs already. It's just a warning because cases have occurred where this has resulted in tragedy. For instance, a ship's master estimated an error (the gyro was broken down) by searching the journal for a similar course. Being still uncertain of the recorded deviation he requested the third officer to check the error immediately the new course was steered.

The officer, when doing this, made an error of observation and/or computation which produced what to him seemed a most unlikely result. Fearing some imaginary criticism from the master the officer confirmed the tentative estimate already suggested. In the event the course steered was 12° in error; the ship ran aground, remained there for a fortnight and the master tendered his resignation. Clearly, no one, least of all the writer, imputes that a young navigator does this sort of thing intentionally or with full knowledge of the possible consequences. If any temptation exists for 'cooking the books' it should be resisted for there is no excuse for any lapse of personal integrity when the safety of the ship, cargo, or the lives aboard may be at stake. When taking compass errors they should be recorded as observed and computed, however improbable the result—or, alternatively, abandoned and another attempt made.

Recording the Entries

Apart from the deck log the deviation journal is probably the most continuous record kept on the bridge and its contents need little explanation to those who use it daily. If one questions its existence no one is at a loss for an answer. It records the errors and deviations of the past as well as the present. The contents usually reveal several very important facts. Firstly, evidence of good compass performance as shown by very small deviations being maintained over a wide range of both courses and latitudes. This typifies the ideal for which one is naturally grateful.

Secondly, the journal records, equally, evidence of bad performance, of excessive deviation and entries which clearly indicate that there is something wrong which might be remedied. Thirdly, there are hundreds of journals which just as clearly indicate the fact that nothing was done about those large deviations, simply because no further comment appears! Fourthly, should unfortunately a ship meet with an accident caused by an error of navigation then it is certain that the journal will be required as an important item of evidence in any subsequent inquiry.

Lastly, the journal is of pertinent interest to the compass adjuster when he is called aboard to exercise his profession.

Instead of the journal being thus a colourful record and history of the ship's prime instrument of navigation it too often assumes a monotone list of repeated observations with little more to enliven its pages. There are thousands of these dull, uninteresting books aboard ships at sea. The monotonous regularity of the entries in the remarks column, such as, 'rolling easily', or 'good steady bearing', provide little to inspire interest or provoke thought. No wonder that when each journal is filled it gets consigned to some dark corner or, perhaps, under the chartroom settee.

The reader is invited to study a few extracts from actual deviation journals. It is hoped he may find them of interest and help to direct his attention to certain entries which, had they been prominently emphasised would have served their purpose better by suggesting to the navigators aboard, or to the professional adjuster, the nature of possible action.

Case 1

Each of the entries listed had, in the original, several others in between not quoted though each was consistent and supported those recorded. The vessel is *en route* from Bahrain in the Persian Gulf to Mombasa, thence to the U.K. via Dakar. The points to note are that the deviations throughout are acceptably low. The range of courses extend from 143°(C) in 26°N at the commencement, through south to 228°(C) in 8½°N to 276°(C) rounding the Cape in 34°S, thence to 340°(C) in 10°S round to 028°(C) in 30°N with a similar course still further north in 52½°N. The deviations are small throughout the voyage, cover a large number of different courses spread over a wide range of latitude and clearly indicate that the compass performance is good, reliable and requires little or no attention. The reader, with a little previous knowledge, will have noted particularly that the deviation on the westerly courses rounding the Cape were quite small, clearly indicating that the separation of B was satisfactory within practical limits.

Throughout the passage the gyro error on the bearing plate used for observations was consistently 2° low.

The ship eventually docked in Manchester. With the final entry for the voyage, might it not have added interest and information to separate the one voyage from the next with a few lines in which appeared a very brief summary, such as:—

'*Standard compass deviations seldom in excess of* $1\frac{1}{2}°$, *usually less than* $1°$ *on courses from* $143°$ *through* $180°$, $270°$ *and* $000°$ *to* $032°$ *over wide range of latitude from Persian Gulf to Irish Sea via the Cape. Recommended adjustment—nil. Gyro error* $2°$ *low might have been removed by resetting repeater.*'

In the event the journal continued on the next line with the next voyage a fortnight later.

Perhaps one might say that nothing needed to be specially mentioned since there appeared to be nothing wrong. On the contrary, for the very reason that the adjustment seemed satisfactory, and the evidence supported it, there was a strong case for emphasising the fact quite prominently so that the master, officers and any future compass adjuster would have their attention drawn to the fact.

Case II

During another passage on the same ship, on one page of the journal there appear no less than 10 mistakes out of 26 entries! Each of these shows a discrepancy in the error obtained from the difference between the true and compass bearings of the observed object. In one of these there is an additional error in the sign of the deviation. None of these observations has been checked for further possible errors of computing the necessary true bearings; the reader may draw his own conclusions and that normal care should be exercised in the mechancis of ascertaining errors and deviations—10 mistakes on one page is a biᵻ high by anyone's standards! The page in question is not illustrated for obvious reasons.

Case III

The same ship, again on another passage round the Cape, some 18 months later, featured the quoted entries. The ship is once more penetrating the southern hemisphere and the standard compass shows increasing deviations approaching the Cape homeward bound and decreasing deviations leaving it. The reader will note the deterioration on the final arrival off the Cape when the ship was heading $282°(C)$. This indicates that on each of the preceding south-westerly courses and the subsequent north-westerly courses the westerly deviation was caused partly by insufficient Flinders bar in the case on the fore side of the binnacle. A clear example of a quick and easy diagnosis. Obviously the equilibrium magnetisation of the

CASE I

DATE	G.M.T.	SHIP'S POSITION LAT.	SHIP'S POSITION LONG.	SHIP'S HEAD GYRO	SHIP'S HEAD STANDARD	SHIP'S HEAD STEERING	BEARING TRUE	BEARING GYRO	BEARING STANDARD	OBJECT	ERROR GYRO	ERROR STANDARD	ERROR STEERING	VARIATION	DEVIATION STANDARD	DEVIATION STEERING	HEEL	REMARKS	OBSERVER
13.1.68	2200	26 08 N	56 48 E	143°	143°		171°T	168	168	Canopus	3° Low	3°E		1½E	1½E			Good bearing	3/o.
17.1.68	1516	8°30'N	51 14 E	226	228		239½°	238	240	☉	1½ L	½ W		1 W	½ E			Good steady bearing	2/o.
20.1.68	0115	22 52	41 18 E	221	224		070	068½	071½	*Arct's	1½ L	1½ W		2¼ W	¾ E			V/L Rolling	C.O
9.2.68	1524	21 15	38 10 E	215	230		271	269½	284½	☉	1½ L	13½ W		13 W	½ W			Good bearing	3/o.
12.2.68	2130	34 12 S	25 53 E	250	276		028½	027	053	Moon	1½ L	24½ W		22½ W	2 W			V/L Rolling & Pitching	2/o.
20.2.68	0230	10 22 S	21 16 W	323	340		256½	254½	271½	*Sirius	2 L	15 W		17 W	2 E			Rolling easily	C.O.
29.3.68	1525	29 37 N	14 25 W	017	028		227	225	236	☉	2 L	11 W		11½ W	½ E			Rolling freely	3/o.
5.3.68	2245	52 23 N	5 26 W	021	032		157	155¾	166¾	Jupiter	1¼ L	9¾ W		10 W	¼ E			Good steady bearing	2/o.

CASE III

DATE	G.M.T.	SHIP'S POSITION LAT.	SHIP'S POSITION LONG.	SHIP'S HEAD GYRO	SHIP'S HEAD STANDARD	SHIP'S HEAD STEERING	BEARING TRUE	BEARING GYRO	BEARING STANDARD	OBJECT	ERROR GYRO	ERROR STANDARD	ERROR STEERING	VARIATION	DEVIATION STANDARD	DEVIATION STEERING	HEEL	REMARKS	OBSERVER
19.10.69	1921	22 05 S	36 58 E	206	222		144½	141	157	*Canopus	½ L	16 W		15 W	1 W			—	3/o
20.10.69	2348	27 16 S	33 27 E	211	235		261½	260½	284½	☾	1 L	23 W		17½ W	5½ W			Good steady low bearing	2/o.
22.10.69	0100	32 19 S	29 05 E	220	248		267	267	295	☽	NIL	28 W		22½ W	5½ W			Good bearing	C.O.
22.10.69	1313	34 21 S	26 00 E	252	282		287	287	317	☉	NIL	30 W		23½ W	6½ W			—"—	C.O.
24.10.69	0141	33 27 S	17 16 E	322	348		293	293	319	☾	Nil	26 W		24 W	2 W			Good bearing	3/o.
26.10.69	0817	23 53 S	08 32 E	322	346.		083	082½	106½	☉	½ L	24 W		21½ W	2½ W			Good steady bearing	2/o.
27.6.69	1432	18 35 S	00 24 E	325	346.		270	270	291	☉	NIL	21 W		20½ W	½ W			Rolling easily	C.O.

FIG. 13

CASE IV		S	E																
24.9.70	0719	2837	1329	144	163.		071¾	071½	090½	☉	¼ L	18¾W		22¾W	4E			Good bearing	3/0.
26.9.70.	0157	3450	2020	077	093		080	080½	096½	✶ SIRIUS.	½ H	16½W		24½W	7¾E			—"—	2/0.
26.9.70.	1300	3426.	2303.	086	102		303	302.	318	☉	1L	15W.		24W.	9E			Good steady brg	2/0.
3.10.70	2200	2136	5625	054	066		098	097	109..	✶ Sirius	1L	.11W		18W	7E			Rolling easily	C.O
6.10.70.	0420	1517	6406	050	059		083	083½	091½	☉	½L	8½W		13¾W	5¼E			Good steady brg.	3/0
10.11.70	0345	1545	5808	225	243		100¼	098¼	116¼	☉	2L	16W		12¾W	3¼W			Good bearing	C.O
11.11.70.	1443	2130	5307	228	252		251¼	250½	274½	☉	¾L	23¼W		16½W	6¾W			Good bearing	3/0.
12.11.70	1130	2418	4830	236	264		270	269½	297½	☉	½L	27½W.		18¾W	8¾W			Good steady brg	2/0.
15.11.70	0053	3030	3400	245	278		331½	331½	004½	☽	NIL	33W		21½W	11½W			Good bearing	C.O.
15.11.70	1300	3118	3?25	245	279		273½	275	309	☉	1½H	35½W		21½W	14.W			Good bearing	3/0.
25.11.70.	0100	3012	3706.	093	106		093	094	107	☾	1H	14W.		22W.	8E			Good steady brg.	2/0.
CASE V																			
24.12.65	1608	1407S	4056E.	359°	006°		108½°	104¾°	111¾°	SIRIUS	¾L	6½W		7½°W	1¼°E			Good steady brg.	2/0.
25.12.65	004.	1244.	4053	359°.	005°		268½°	268°	274°.	RIGEL	½°L.	5½W.		6½W	1E			—"—	2/0.
6.11.66	0513	0134 S.	4246	049	048		115	114	113	☉	1°L	2E		3W	5E			Good steady brg	C.O.
6.1.66.	1901	0009 N	4448	047°	046°		165½°	165°	164°	Canopus	½°L	1½°E		3W	4½E			Good bearing.	3/0,
7.1.66.	0021	0040 N	4521E	047	045		004¾	004½	002½	DUBHE	¼E	2¼E		1¾W	4E			Good bearing	C.O.
7.1.66.	1922.	0259	4732.	051°	049°		250½	250	248	Diphda	½L.	2½E		3½W	5E			Good bearing.	3/0.
8.1.66.	0022	0356	4836	051°	049°		002½	002½	000½	DUBHE	NIL	2E		1¼W	3¼E			Good steady brg.	C.O.
8.1.66	0520	0425	4906.	022°	020°		119½	119	117	☉	½L	2½E		2½W	5E			—"—	C.O.
10.1.66.	0028	1209N	5039E	272°	274°		247½°	246½	248½	SIRIUS	1°L.	1°W		NIL	1°W			Good bearing	2/0.
11.1.66.	1537.	1402N	4157E	313°	313°		110½°	110°	111°	Sirius	½°L.	½°W		½E	1°W			Good bearing.	3/0,

Fig. 14

ship had undergone a slow but steady change since the rather better performance illustrated in Case 1.

But no one's attention is directed to this in the journal. Why not? Why not insert a suitable endorsement on the next but one line, such as:—

'Information for the attention of compass adjuster. Growth of deviation on westerly courses in southern latitudes caused by insufficient Flinders bar. Suggested action: examine and lengthen.'

If such a note is further emphasised with red underlining, etc., it would not be easily overlooked but would instead attract the attention immediately of anyone perusing the journal. It might even conceivably cause someone to take the opportunity of altering the length of Flinders bar on a tentative basis and actually remove the offending deviation! But that would be asking too much and would entail having another look under that chartroom settee for the spare bits of Flinders bar, all covered in dust. If this were, however, done—a further note should be made in the journal to this effect, quoting date, time, position and precise action taken for future reference. Supporting error and deviation observations would then follow to indicate the improvement and the removal of the deviation.

Case IV

This is an extract on another voyage exactly a year later. There is no record of any compass adjustment either by the master or by a professional adjuster having been undertaken. The ship is once more rounding the Cape, this time east-bound; the deterioration is now more pronounced. Note that the deviations are now easterly as expected—but nothing is done. A month later the ship did two trips across the Indian Ocean between East London and Madras and then on to Japan. By this time the deviations on easterly and westerly courses in latitude 30°S, approximately, had grown to 11°, 12° and 14°!

The list of deviations continues with every subsequent entry confirming that the adjustment done some two-and-a-half years ago is no longer effective. But the entries are routine and no one worries (cares?); still less is there a separate entry, such as:—

'This compass needs careful readjustment—particularly the Flinders bar, which appears to be heavily undercompensating.

Recommended action—increase the length of the Flinders bar and keep close check on deviation.'

If additional entries of this nature are made someone is surely bound to read them eventually and perhaps there is one with sufficient courage, and the physical strength, to carry a lump of Flinders bar on to the compass platform, put it on top of what he finds already in the brass case, and set matters right.

Case V

On a voyage between Mombasa and Suez, not far from the magnetic equator, the extract from the journal shows some interesting features.

The deviations on courses close to 000°(C) are small and easterly while those on courses close to 270°(C) are small and westerly. These might indicate small residual values of +B and +C due mainly to permanent magnetism on account of the insignificant value of Z in these latitudes.

Nevertheless, the deviation appears to grow in the north-east quadrant. This might be due partly to semi-circular deviation because both coefficients tend to accumulate easterly deviation on 045°(C) though not quite to the extent observed.

The excess deviation is probably quadrantal, requiring the spheres fractionally nearer to the compass. This would seem to be partly confirmed with the last entry quoted where the semi-circular deviation would approach zero in the north-west quadrant where +B and +C cause deviation of opposite sign. The residual westerly deviation appearing seems to confirm the D to be slightly undercompensated.

If the significance of the observed deviations had been noticed a further entry in the deviation journal would not have been out of place. At a future date a professional adjuster would welcome remarks of that nature and naturally help him during the readjustment. Of course, the master or any of his navigators qualified to do so, could do little harm by slacking the holding down bolts and setting each sphere half an inch or so closer to the compass in anticipation. He would also have the added advantage, being on the spot, of studying the subsequent deviations during the next passage to tell him if there was an improvement.

If this was obtained then another suitable entry should be made in the journal to that effect; and again underlined in red, properly timed and dated. The dull, monotonous and

DATE	TIME	LAT	LONG	GYRO Reading	GYRO Error	TRUE Hdg.	VAR.	MAG. Hdg.	MAGNETIC COMPASSES Standard	MAGNETIC COMPASSES TMC	COMPASS DEVIATION Standard	COMPASS DEVIATION TMC
CASE VI												
12-1-72	1130	28N	16W	194°	1E	195°	11.5W	206.5	206°	207°	0.5E	0.5W
12.1.72	2200	25N	17W	193°	1E	194°	12W	206°	206°	207°	0°	1.0E
14-1-72	1000	16N	18W	179°	1E	180°	13.5W	193.5	190°	192°	3.5E	1.5E
15.1.72	2100	7N	16W	140°	1E	141°	15W	156	148°	150°	8E	6E
17.1.72	2030	3S	8W	141°	1E	142°	13.5E	128.5	141°	150°	9.5W	7.5E
24-1-72	2200	35.5S	21E	062°	1W	081°	24W	105	080°	057°	25E	54E
25.1.72	2300	33.5S	28E	057°	0°	066°	23W	019°	059°	038°	20E	41E
26-1-72	1100	32.5S	30.5E	057°	1W	052°	22W	078	058°	036°	20E	42E
28.1.72	2200	19.5S	41E	018°	0°	017°	11°E	028	021°	010°	7E	18E
30.1-72	2200	8S	45E	029°	1W	028°	4.5W	032.5	028°	018°	4.5E	14.5E

Date	Time												
1.2.72	1000	1°N	50°E	025°	1°W	034°	3°N	026°	026°	033°	015°	3½E	11°E
4.2.72	1000	18°N	58°E	027°	3°W	026°	0	026°	026°	025°	021°	1°E	5°E
5.2.72	2400	26°N	52°E	273°	2°E	273°	1°E	269°	269°	266°	265°	3°E	4°E
6.2.72	2000	21°N	50°E	225°	1°E	226°	1.5°E	224.5°	224°	224°	223°	0.5°E	1.5°E
10.2.72	2200	21°N	59°E	202°	1°E	203°	0	203°	203°	286°	1°E	3°W
11.2.72	2300	15°N	52°E	206°	1°E	207°	6.5°W	207.5°	310°	312°	2.5°W	4.5°W
13.2.72	2200	5°N	57°E	205°	1°E	206°	15°W	207.5°	311°	316°	3.5°W	8.5°W
16.2.72	1000	9°S	44°E	206°	1°E	207°	5.5°W	210.5°	220°	228°	7.5°W	13.5°W
17.2.72	1000	15°S	41°E	203°	1°E	204°	8°W	213°	226°	244°	14°W	29°W
19.2.72	1000	24°S	36°E	226°	1°E	227°	14°W	241°	267°	280°	26°W	3°+
20.2.72	1000	28°S	35°E	223°	1°E	224°	19.5°W	243.5°	269°	264°	24.5°W	40.5°W

FIG. 15

uninspired record of errors comes alive every now and then with such special entries; all to good purpose, and not just for the fun of it.

Case VI

Whilst there is a limit to the space available for reproducing extracts from journals readers, many of whom it is hoped are aboard ship as they read this, could hardly fail to be impressed and no doubt horrified by the tabulated results shown for Case VI. Admittedly the ship was both brand new and very large; initially adjusted in Japan and fitted with a standard compass on the compass platform, and a transmitting compass in the wheelhouse. One would not expect the initial adjustment to be maintained during the first year of service. Subtle changes in the equilibrium magnetisation of the ship would be anticipated.

Certainly coefficient B would be expected to give some trouble. So, in a sense, it is not surprising that substantial deviations should appear when the ship arrives in an area most likely to promote them. The deviations did appear, as can be seen.

But once the evidence was clear and undisputed, why was nothing done about it aboard? Thirty, forty and fifty degrees of deviation—and no action taken—it's incredible! What price the directive field strength northward under such circumstances? It's a wonder that the compass pointed anywhere! And who was responsible in the first place for putting an expensive transmitting magnetic compass in such an obviously deficient magnetic location? The magnetic conditions were never investigated—they couldn't have been—they seldom are, whatever the books say about it. One thing is certain—it couldn't have been a *steady* compass. But that's not the worst of it. The standard compass had a length of Flinders bar on the fore side—obviously much too short—why didn't someone lengthen the thing? Didn't they know? They were qualified officers, surely? Were they paralysed—perhaps with fear? The TMC had a Flinders bar on the *after* side! Not content with under-compensation, the corrector was increasing the deviation to double the value it might have been with no Flinders bar there at all! This was magnetic madness, but the most astonishing thing of all was that nothing was *done* about it! But they kept the records, bless them, and were no doubt proud in a perverse sort of way of having a compass pointing more than 50° away from magnetic north.

Perhaps the reader is amused, though it isn't particularly funny and it might be thought pathetic. So, before one is tempted to say—'it can't happen to me'—might it not be a good idea to have a look at your own journal and examine those deviations rounding the Cape, or in the Australian Bight? The records provide the evidence and those quoted in these pages are only a few among too many to count. But human nature is very odd and in the writer's experience there have been many similar instances reported with some peculiar pride in the fact that no action was taken when it should have been. Cases are reported almost with relish and seem to say—'we had a shocking compass—we let the rot develop—we cherished every extra degree of deviation—we recorded them all for everyone to see—and then we sat back in a kind of death-wish, hoping that the gyro would break down when we needed it most, and waited to pursue our next course coast-wise with a minimum margin of safety.' What is it that makes otherwise sensible and efficient officers almost like imbeciles with cases like these?

It has been said—'never mind the academic stuff—all this theory—the hypothetical cases which never happen—the improbable sums to work out which bear little or no relation to what really happens aboard ship—let's have the practical things, they say—something where common sense (does that mean intelligence?) prevails.' Well, you've got it now! And when you scan those entries in your own journal don't be too disappointed when you can't find values more than 10° or 15°— it's only relative. Only the superlatively indifferent can muster 50° of deviation; the less incompetent must remain content with 15°.

The Deviation Journal

Case VI takes the biscuit in more senses than one.

Have you noticed the column headings? They are based entirely on *heading references*, so that the errors, and deviations, at the magnetic compass positions were obtained apparently from corrected gyro courses with the variation applied.

Complete and blind reliance placed upon the accuracy of the lubber marks on one repeater and two compasses any, or all of which, could have been in error. And not a bearing of any kind taken; at least not of which there is any record!

Presumably somewhere along the line the gyro error was observed—or was this another assumption? Apart from the startling facts revealed it seems that this type of journal sets out one of the worst possible arrangements of column headings. This raises the question as to who decides how these books should be printed?

Is any effort made to ensure a foolproof record?

If so, by whom? Whose responsibility is it to have an accurate record of deviation? Obviously, the hapless master takes this responsibility. What can he do about it other than recommend that column headings should be printed differently by the suppliers of these books? He may indeed recommend, but will anything be done about it?

Perhaps the simplest way out is to cross out undesirable headings and write in new ones, more suitable. Two conclusions emerge from these records. The error and deviation at the standard magnetic compass should be observed and recorded *solely at that compass*, i.e. bearings should be taken at the standard compass and referred to nothing else. Secondly, the only heading comparison permissible is to compare a separate steering magnetic compass with the standard compass where both are fitted, simply because it is usually almost impossible to take observations directly at such a compass. The lubber lines of each compass should be checked to see that they individually mark the position of the bow of the ship. Gyro errors must be taken *entirely separately* and not used as a means for comparison.

These are the facts—not points for debate or opinion—they must be faced. Finally, every entry should name the body observed (and the body observing!) so that if necessary, at an inquiry for instance, the true bearing can be calculated and checked at a later date should the necessity arise.

'Rolling Easily'

The last word lies in the matter of unsteady compasses in a seaway which implies, among other things, uncorrected heeling error. Most journals have a column headed 'heel'. This is an odd title because no one knows what to put down.

Usually it's 'nil' or R.E., short for 'rolling easily'! It provides practically no information.

Heeling error, as such, seldom, if ever, occurs—but the unsteadiness produced by uncompensated forces shows up prominently on northerly and southerly courses. Perhaps this is where the 'remarks' column might come in, instead of the usual comment about a 'good steady bearing'.

When the ship is rolling on courses near to both north and south the card should be observed for several minutes, the amount by which the card swings each side of the lubber mark carefully estimated, and the period of roll observed with a watch. A distinction should, of course, be made between genuine unsteadiness and the effects of yaw. The results can be usefully included in the journal so that someone is encouraged to re-adjust the heeling error correctors until the card is steady once more. Yet another special note would then be recorded in the journal to that effect, so that everyone would know what was done and when.

The State of the Art and Safety

What has been stated here is, in a sense, an act of appeasement directed towards those who dislike theoretical descriptions presented by armchair navigators, and who much prefer to deal with things on a practical level. And yet, it is possible that the foregoing paragraphs which describe and illustrate the practice of so simple an operation as observing and recording errors and deviations, have not altogether pleased the officer who has just read them. He has suffered reading about:

   (i) Treating the whole business as a bad habit.

  (ii) Taking bearings on a gyro repeater and making it appear that he took them at a standard compass.

 (iii) Being too tired to go on the compass platform.

  (iv) Assuming that three or more lubber lines all marked the sharp end of the ship when none of them was verified.

   (v) Junior officers who have been known to think that two wrongs made a right.

  (vi) Records of deviation unsupported by the data recorded.

 (vii) Compass deviation journals with column headings which encourage loose practice and doubtful procedures.

(viii) Compass deviations growing to alarming values and no action taken.

  (ix) Uninspired records with little or no comment and emphasis about salient features, en route adjustments, and adjustments done by professional adjusters.

   (x) No effective record of either unsteadiness caused by uncorrected rolling errors, or, remedies taken.

The state of the art is not very creditable. To be sure, there is a minority who would claim the criticisms are unnecessary, even unjust. This must be so, because there are always exceptions and among them navigators who recognise bad habits, do not form them and perform their duties by being in touch with reality. The reader is left to judge for himself, not with what should or should not be done by others, but what *he does himself* to ensure an efficient stand-by magnetic compass on *his ship*. It is for the reader to judge the state of his *own art*, not someone else's, and then decide if he has contributed towards greater safety at sea, or merely added an additional hazard for want of careful thought and better judgement. Surely, it is better to be compass-wise than compass-foolish.

CHAPTER 8

Deviations which Do Not Exist.

One of the most familiar navigational routines practised aboard ship is to check the compass error. After applying magnetic variation the end product is deviation for ship's head on the magnetic compass and, in the case of the gyro the constant error of the bearing plate. Both of these, it is hoped, are small so that reasonably accurate courses can be made and the compasses used for position finding in the usual way. The procedures are both simple and well known, but are they reliable? If not, to what extent are the results of observation to be questioned and how may this affect navigation?

The Usual Practice

THE normal practice aboard ship, as every navigator knows, is to observe for deviation and gyro error at least once each watch and more often when courses are changed. The records are entered in the deviation journal and the errors applied for setting courses and taking bearings. The most likely reference is either the Sun or a star and the methods of computing are a standard routine. The effect of this procedure, repeated frequently, is to accumulate a series of deviations on given courses in often widely-different latitudes. There is, in consequence, a dearth of recorded deviations on different courses within close limits of latitude.

With some exceptions this is to be expected; at least it has the value of knowing what deviation might occur on a required course at the time that it is needed.

What is not indicated is the reliability of the observed deviation beyond the fairly close agreement reached by successive watchkeepers during the voyage.

It may be useful to examine what actually happens to ascertain the possible errors of both observation and computation and the means by which some of these can be found and, so far as is possible, interpreted.

67

Personal Error

Successive officers of the watch usually agree on the amount of deviation within acceptable limits. Even so, on the same course, the recorded entries may often differ by as much as two degrees; occasionally more.

With single observations of this kind it is difficult and practically impossible to ascertain the cause of discrepancy. Nevertheless, it is useful to appreciate the possible areas of error. These may be listed as follows.

(i) The ability to *observe* the compass bearing to an accuracy of half a degree.

With a *steady compass* and the ship not rolling heavily, most officers can observe a bearing accurately provided the observed body is not too high in the sky. Anything closer than half degree seems to be an ambitious claim. Conversely, to make an accurate observation at a compass not properly corrected for heeling error when the ship is rolling heavily is virtually impossible, especially on courses close to 000° and 180°.

(ii) The instant of observation can be quite critical. If GMT or accurate Zone Time is carried on the wrist the time interval between compass platform and the chronometer is of no concern. On the other hand estimates made without the use of a stop-watch can be in error and subsequently affect the computed true azimuth through an error in the local hour angle. This is particularly the case when the rate of change of azimuth is greatest. The worst condition for observing is clearly when the body is near its upper meridian passage. To reduce time interval error it is wise to choose broad azimuths coupled with low altitudes.

(iii) Whatever tables may be used to ascertain the true azimuth, it is certain that the Nautical Almanac is essential to gain both local hour angle and declination.

Each item together with the latitude must be accurate. These ingredients used in conjunction with the azimuth or ABC tables provide an accurate true azimuth. It is probable at this stage that most personal errors are induced through approximate working. If azimuth tables are used the correct methods of interpolation are seldom employed because they are ponderous and there is a strong tendency to 'round off' the latitude to the nearest half degree; to treat the declination likewise, and adjust the hour angle to fit! Often, a 'hit and miss' process causes the navigator to dodge between columns for declination and between pages for latitude, and then 'estimate' the true azimuth by some intuitive 'bracketing' system. The final azimuth upon which so much depends can easily be half a degree in error through such a process. The ABC enthusiasts also fall into the trap of interpolating casually instead of accurately. For safety it is wise to interpolate A, B and C to the third place of decimals. After all, the true azimuth computed for a given instant should be the one factor over which there should be no dispute whatever. Unfortunately, in the event, it may be the one item most suspect.

(iv) In the case of magnetic compasses the magnetic *variation* must be applied to the observed error to ascertain the deviation, as everyone knows. Here again personal integrity is to some degree at stake because loose practice may very easily produce an error in the variation. When navigating coastwise the larger scale charts often feature compass roses in two or more local areas. Depending upon the disposition of these with respect to own ship's position some navigators interpret the variation far too casually by considering proportionate distances between known values *without any regard to the orientation of the isogonic lines in the region.*

Correctly, the small scale variation chart must be consulted in conjunction with the larger scale navigational chart to determine the orientation of the lines of equal value. In this sense the navigational chart can be quite misleading and inaccurate values of the variation estimated which in turn are reflected in the deviation for ship's head.

Clearly, this is a personal affair and distinguishes a good navigator from a casual one; particularly coastwise navigators who seldom see the need for consulting the variation charts when in fact it is they who should be most concerned.

A further scource of error can be caused by up-dating the variation inaccurately; sometimes the process must be *reversed* when the variation is quoted for a *future* date. Variation charts of the latest epoch should always be used and many of these display the new type of isallogonic curves over-printed on the isogonals.

Attention to these several points will tend to produce deviations observed by successive watchkeepers which are in closer agreement than those often appearing in the deviation journal. Of course, in spite of great care and proper usage it is still possible to apply the wrong variation through no fault of the navigator simply because its value may be anomalous. One would be over-optimistic to assume that the variation depicted was in fact precisely the charted value along every foot of a line extending thousands of miles! Departures from the stated value remain unknown except in coastal areas where cautionary notes and advice in the sailing directions give specific information.

Summarising the possible personal errors of observation and computing during normal bridge routine it is unlikely that the recorded deviations are accurate to within,

  (i) 0·5° when observing the bearing.

 (ii) 0·2° when estimating the time of observation.

(iii) 0·5° when effecting the computation using tables and the Nautical Almanac.

(iv) An unknown quantity due to anomalous variation or inaccurately assessed variation.

This means that unless great care is exercised over items (i), (ii) and (iii) they may accumulate and throw doubt on the value of the deviation which may well exceed one degree. The same applies to the gyro error except for the incidence of variation. Fortunately examination of journals shows that successive observations by watchkeeping officers are in closer agreement when finding the gyro error and somewhat less agreement in the matter of deviation. This seems to point once more to the magnetic variation being the item most suspect though not necessarily through the fault of inaccurate estimation from the charts.

Constant Error in the Deviation

Whilst the recorded deviations at a magnetic compass are subject to some inaccuracy on account of personal factors which may with care be avoided there is still no means of ascertaining the presence or absence of any constant deviation, real or apparent, which might affect the compass. The writer wishes, in this instance, to direct attention to other possible causes of inaccurate deviations which may lie submerged or hidden within the observed deviation and therefore never come to light. It is useful, therefore, at the outset to know how to determine a constant deviation if it exists and then to decide what may be done about it.

Coefficient A—How to Find It

Of the thousands of observed deviations recorded in the journals of ships all over the world practically none of them provide the proper means of ascertaining the mean deviation over a complete swing, at least not without considerable trouble. Nevertheless all that is required to find the mean deviation is to make observations on three or more equidistant headings. The mean is then called the approximate co-efficient A.

The mean of the deviations observed on *any* three headings, each separated from the next by 120°, will suffice. Although three is the minimum from which the value may be found, it is easier (and probably more natural) in practice to observe the deviation on each of the *four cardinal* headings instead. In the cause of accuracy the mean of the deviations on 8, 16 or 32 headings might be preferable but would be tedious and time-consuming and the opportunity of doing so generally un-favourable.

The Mean Compass Error and the Mean Deviation

Since the total error from true north at a magnetic compass is the combined effect of the variation and the deviation it follows that the mean compass error is 'Variation +A'. If it is then assumed that the variation is accurately known from the chart the value of A can be established. If on the other hand some doubt exists regarding the variation, e.g. an anomalous value conflicts with the chart then the mean compass error contains the variation and some constant deviation neither of which can be determined without first scientifically ascertaining the true variation. The latter is not an easy proposition aboard ship.

These several considerations point to the significance of the mean deviation. Having taken time out, perhaps at anchor or swinging to successive changes of the tide, the deviations are observed, the mean taken and the value of coefficient A found. What then are the likely causes of it?

Coefficient Real A

There are rare occasions when a magnetic compass is 'badly situated' by which is meant that through special circumstances it is impossible to secure a symmetrical distribution of superstructure surrounding the compass. Any type of craft which precludes the placing of the compass on the fore and aft *centre* line, such as an aircraft carrier, destroys the symmetry of structure either local or general and this has the effect of introducing certain coefficients which would otherwise be absent. Among these is coefficient A. The asymmetry referred to could of course occur where the compass itself is 'well placed' on the fore and aft centre-line but has some asymmetric structure, like a radar tower, offset from the centre-line and not very far away. In such cases the constant mean deviation is termed a 'real' coefficient A because it is due to the magnetic influence of the ship and causes genuine deviation of the compass needle. In this connection yacht compasses often suffer from such nearby interference. In these cases there is little one can do because the damage has already been done. Initial planning and bridge design might have helped to prevent it occurring in the first place.

Although constant deviation is the present subject of discussion it might be mentioned, for those who have previous knowledge of the causes of deviation, that whenever horizontally disposed high permeability effects cannot be arranged symmetrically about *any vertical plane* through the compass then coefficients real A and E will both have values. This means that the imposed deviation pattern can be made the subject of separate deviation analysis consisting of two parts, a constant deviation and a quadrantal deviation which reaches a maximum on the cardinal headings.

The amounts of each would clearly depend upon circumstances but the point to bear in mind is that no case exists for random deviations. Every case can be submitted to analysis and some value for the two coefficients will emerge.

If therefore, the mean deviation has a magnetic origin the causes of which cannot be removed the question arises as to whether this constant deviation can be eliminated, or even corrected.

The answer to this is clearly 'yes' because an appropriate asymmetric arrangement of high permeability bars of ferrous metal can be placed to cause a constant deviation of equal amount and opposite sign.

Unfortunately, although it is possible no provision is made for this on an approved type of binnacle so that any such arrangement would need to be improvised. The absence of any facility is however justified because there is usually no real A present.

This is reasonable since some care is recommended and, it is hoped, taken to see that the compass is well sited.

Coefficient Apparent A

Perhaps the most interesting thing about coefficient A is the fact that certain personal errors (referred to above) and mechanical errors of equipment used can contribute to the mean deviation being other than zero. In this event the mean deviation consists of two parts, (i) Real or Magnetic A already referred to and, (ii) 'Apparent' A, which may be due to one or all of several causes none of which is due to magnetism but all attributed to some fault in the methods of observing and computing. The colloquial term 'Apparent' A is most apt in the sense that an error of some kind which *appears* to exist is not necessarily present in fact.

The paradox is justified if only to distinguish between genuine magnetic effects causing deviation and other processes which have that *appearance*. The possible causes of an apparent A coefficient, apart from those mentioned under Personal Error might be listed as follows,

(a) Non-parallelism between the line joining the 000° and 180° marks on the card and the magnetic axis of the compass element. This is effectively impossible in practice because cards are graduated to an accuracy of 0·5° (M. 616/72, Appendix I, paragraph 16a).

(b) The displacement of the lubber's mark to one side or the other from the true fore and aft line of the ship.

This introduces a definite error in the heading reference when *steering courses*. Also, when comparing one compass with another spurious deviations can occur if headings are compared simply because of the possible displacement of either or both lubber's lines. *These inaccuracies cannot affect bearings.*

(c) An error in the azimuth taking device would alter all observed bearings to the extent of the malajustment.

Summary

If coefficient A is determined from the mean of the deviations on, say, the cardinal headings, it may then be either 'real' or 'apparent' or a mixture of the two incapable of separation. In practice, with a well-placed compass, it is most likely to be an apparent deviation caused by personal error in observing and/or computing, (i), (ii), (iii) and (iv) above, or a mechanical deficiency as suggested in (a), (b) and (c) above. The least likely of the several sources of constant deviation are the magnetic causes of coefficient A together with the listed items (a) and (c). The only other likelihood of mistakenly introducing an apparent A is through the misuse of a variation setting control (VSC) if fitted. This provision is unlikely except on certain transmitting compasses where great care must be exercised.

Precautions and Remedies

The obvious action to reduce the constant deviation is to take as much care as possible in computing the true azimuth. Loose practice when using the Almanac and associated tables should be substituted with more careful working. The observed bearing should be as accurate as possible compatible with the circumstances and the magnetic variation estimated with due regard to the orientation of the isogonals in the area. Deviations should never be assessed by comparing heading references unless the location of the lubber's marks have been positively checked. The standard magnetic compass should not be compared directly with a gyro bearing repeater unless, again, the *lubber's marks of each have been verified*. Where there are separate standard and steering magnetic compasses fitted there is no alternative to course comparison; verification of the lubber's marks is essential in such a case. If, after these precautions, a constant deviation determined by analysis still persists little can be done and it should then be recorded in the journal as an *index error* to be applied to all future deviations regardless of the part of the world in which they are observed.

If any lubber's mark is found to be displaced it should, of course, be restored to the fore and aft line by slewing the binnacle fractionally. The same should be done with the gyro bearing repeater pedestal. Since the adjustment entails a movement of only one degree or so none of the magnetic compensations already made are upset. It follows that any residual apparent A which occurs at a steering compass can be treated likewise by slewing the binnacle.

In this connection the most vulnerable parts of the compass equipment are bridge-wing gyro repeaters. Carefully taped reference marks should be placed on deck as far forward as possible to ensure a perfect alignment.

The azimuth-taking device is rarely the cause of inaccurate bearings. The 'arrow up' and 'arrow down' test can be made quite easily to verify that the bearings of a low altitude object taken by each method agree.

Should there be a discrepancy it is not always easy to adjust an azimuth mirror because adjusting screws are not generally provided and it might be necessary to improvise with very thin liners of brass inserted under the horizontal axis spindle supporting the frame of the reflecting prism.

Index Errors

The practising navigator aboard ship accepts as routine such things as determining the index error of his sextant, or of the barometer; but practically no effort is made to do the same for the magnetic compass. It is perhaps another of those blind spots; something not to bother about because no one told us to.

The cumulative effects can, of course, amount to two or even three degrees. If the navigator is unaware of them one might say that no great harm is done and the subsequent displacement of the ship from the intended track attributed to some unknown set of the current. Be that as it may—in the open ocean it doesn't matter, but a fast passage in coastal water is a different thing altogether when the course made good to the nearest degree is quite critical and may affect the safety of the ship.

CHAPTER 9

Mysterious, Unpredictable and Unwanted Deviation.

This series of essays has provided an encouraging response from a number of masters and navigating officers aboard ship which has tempted the author to invite those who may wish to undertake an investigation into retentive error; something which has hitherto been largely a matter of hearsay and speculation.

The Mood of the Moment

We live in a curious age in which it is difficult sometimes to keep the feet on the ground. Everything changes in a fast-moving world and everyone is scrambling to keep pace. The navigator aboard ship must conform to the changing pattern or be left behind; but this does not mean that he should abandon his judgement and accept solely what is thrust on him and disregard matters which, perhaps, deserve his valued consideration.

The times we live in are also conspicuous by the deluge of words which assail us from every quarter. Of course, the written word which has been with us the longest, at least has the virtue of permanence, and can be studied at leisure. But in addition the spoken word is broadcast, televised, recorded and then directed at every living being throughout the day and most of the night. Often the subject matter is battered to death and in some cases more is written and spoken than is known. This can even occur under the umbrella of Education, Training and Research. The practising navigator should be on his guard against an army of armchair navigators who have long-since forgotten what salt water is like, but who are nevertheless anxious to tell him what he should do, why he should do it (as if he didn't know), and having done it why he should have done it some other way. Seldom is the boot on the other foot. It would seem appropriate that for once the navigator at sea might reciprocate and turn the tables. The writer is encouraged to believe this because of the unsolicited, and therefore the more welcome, response to suggestions made in this series of essays to do something compass-wise or, better still, something wise with the compass. In case the reader feels that he is about to be conned into something unreal or pointless, let it be said immediately that a number of masters and officers have taken the opportunity of doing some minor adjustments to their magnetic compasses and apparently, judging by their reports, even enjoyed the success of their efforts. There may be a number who have tried likewise about whom we do not know; it is hoped that they met with the same satisfaction. In this mood and in this spirit of co-operation a proposition appears below which may tempt officers on the bridge, but not before the reasons for the proposal are explained.

Anticipated Deviation

The theory of deviation at a magnetic compass permits observed deviation in one locality to be forecast for another or, better still, eliminated before it has an opportunity to reappear. At a *well-corrected* compass few problems exist because in the event of a gyro breakdown the fact that only small deviations are present permits good courses to be made and allows the use of a nice steady compass, even in a seaway, both for steering purposes and position fixing. The fact that the sky may be clouded causes no concern and there is apparently no immediate necessity to check the error beyond the routine normally observed once the sky clears again. The point being made is that the causes of deviation and their elimination are well understood withing the framework of the subject which abhors any form of random or disorganised deviation being possible. A well-corrected compass, working efficiently, cannot spring any surprises—or can it?

Mysterious and Unpredictable Deviation

Unfortunately the compass can, from time to time, alarm the navigator with apparently unpredictable deviation at a time when one might expect otherwise. We refer especially to those occasions when substantially the same course has been maintained across an ocean for several days, the ship approaches a congested area, has to use the magnetic compass because of a gyro failure and is precluded from checking the deviation because of cloud. A large alteration of course becomes necessary and it is then found, from radio position-fixing systems, that the ship is no longer making the required course and that corrected bearings fail to come in with Decca fixes and the like. In such cases untoward deviation is suspected (and later confirmed) or, in the absence of electronic-fixing aids, the ship's course is presumed to be accurate when in fact it isn't by an amount far too great for future safety further along the intended track! Clearly, deviations of the kind can be, and have often reported to have been, a severe embarrassment in many instances. They are to some extent mysterious and certainly unpredictable and seem, on the face of it, to conflict with the explicit theory surrounding the subject. The navigator needs to know more. He needs to know the likely circumstances which cause a compass to misbehave in this fashion; the extent and sign of the deviation likely to occur; the duration of its existence; whether it can be ascertained or anticipated; even removed. He needs, in short, much more information about this odd phenomenon. One thing is clear from the start; there is nothing wrong with the compass because it responds faithfully to the horizontal component of field at that position. The search must lie with the strength, direction and, above all, with the character of the *ship's magnetic influence* to find some evidence of this anomaly.

The Ship's Magnetisation

From the time that the theory of deviation was established in the middle of the last century the character of the ship's magnetisation was assumed to be due partly to low permeability material and the remaining proportion to high permeability material. The former was established by the degrees of violence which occurred during the building process, while the latter was an instantaneous response to the ambient earth's field and featured as vectors of the earth's influence related to preferred ship directions. These ideas, of course, still obtain and lead to the system of compass correction in use today and devised by Lord Kelvin many years ago. The fact that compasses need readjusting from time to time points out, however, that the concept is not perfect; a fact realised very early on in the business. Furthermore, it led to the hull of 19th-century vessels being considered as acquiring a somewhat simple pattern of magnetisation related to induction by the earth's field appropriate to the orientation of the ship on the slipway and the hemisphere in which it was built. This simple concept provided the means of making a tentative forecast of the signs of coefficients B and C, which were related to the 'ship's head when building'. Some vague references to 'local structures', such as the rudder-post, for compasses located aft, possibly providing a predominating effect were made, but this is about as far as it went. In the writer's experience this doubtful emphasis on the importance of the 'building head' persisted well into the 1940s. Little account was taken of the compass *position* and still less of the effect of Z induction during the building process which is probably the principal factor governing the sign of P force acquired at the time of building. Even today some folk with fairly long memories promulgate ideas which are heavily dated and quite unnecessarily emphasise the importance of the 'building head' when, in fact, the topic is of no interest to the practical adjuster and is best forgotten.

'Soft Iron Masts and Derricks'?

To the simple iron hulls of the old vessels were added local superstructures. Progress has increased their number, shape and character. At first such structures were assumed to exhibit a highly-permeable character of magnetisation which led to beams, pillars, posts, derricks, funnels and masts being identified with 'soft' iron material. Such ideas at least recognised that the field at the compass position was affected not solely by the hull but by structures much closer to the compass. Nevertheless, these ideas too, have been popular until quite recent times and there are those even today who make these specific identifications in spite of the fact that the modern construction of ships, where even whole sections and superstructures are often constructed separately from the slipway, can have no relation whatever to the ship's head building, nor any reason for them being highly permeable.

Magnetic Instability

Returning to the pioneers in the study of ship magnetisation and to the slow changes which occur, it was recognised towards the end of the last century that while the magnetism acquired during building was never entirely lost it was somewhat unstable for a considerable time, but that the rate of change decreased as time went by until after a year or two it became essentially permanent. This transitory stage caused Sir George Airy, F.R.S., the then Astronomer Royal, to use the term 'sub-permanent magnetism', and this expressive phrase has been freely used well into this century. Clearly, this unsettled condition was due to changes of the *effective permeability* of the ship's magnetic material. It led to frequent observations of *changes* in the *semi-circular* deviation after dry-docking, being laid-up, or steaming on one course for a long time followed by a bold alteration of the course. Vibration from engines, propellers and the working of the ship in a seaway contributed to these changes of deviation. All the early literature of the subject refers to these untoward deviations, the fact that they cannot be easily forecast and that no means were available to prevent them occurring. A case in point is the Naval Lieutenant who, between 1867 and 1870 investigated these odd deviations during firing practices in one of H.M. ships off Plymouth. He came to the same conclusions and observed that—'it would be of general service if this subject were made one of special observation and comment in the compass journals of ships; this would first serve the immediate practical ends of the seaman, and afterwards furnish the elements of scientific investigation'. If these words, written over a hundred years ago, were true then it may come as a surprise to the reader to learn that they are equally true today! Effectively nothing has been done to provide the profession with serious information about these temporary, transient and highly-embarrassing deviations. Every reference to them is almost casual. Masters and officers acknowledge their existence and quote vaguely their experience. The books which deal with the subject are likewise inconclusive; the deviations are suspected and the sense is quoted invariably as a tendency for the ship to 'remember her old course'. Even the Admiralty Compass Observatory has no organised and tabulated data. Guesswork, innuendo, speculation, plus a few inspired guesses and shrewd estimates are the sum total of information available (not easily) on a topic which clearly can affect the safety of a ship! One hundred years—and nothing done about it. Perhaps it's never too late—or, perhaps it's too late already when the ship has run ashore. Surely, someone ought to have done something about this long since, and because it is information which is needed it can only be obtained 'in the field' and on the bridge. The reader suspects, rightly, that an appeal is directed to navigators aboard ship as the only persons competent, sufficiently skilled and in the right place to provide it.

Contemporary Ideas about Ship Magnetisation

Before any firm proposals are put to the active professional it seems that he should know briefly some of the present thoughts about ship magnetisation. Normally, the magnetisation of a ship is described with reference to the three preferred directions: forward, to starboard and towards the keel. Effective permeabilities are assumed for the three components of induction and certain conclusions reached. The effects of the demagnetising field in each direction is considered and since these are functions of shape a ship is identified simply but sensibly with an ellipsoid whose lengthwise axis, athwartship axis and to-keel axis are nearly in the proportion of 100 : 10 : 6. These provide demagnetising factors in the approximate ratio of 1 : 12 : 18 respectively. If it is now assumed that the value of μ (permeability) of the steel of the ship is of the order of 5000 taking account of the violence caused by the building process, and that the cross-section of the ship occupied by magnetic material is about 1/100 of the total, the *effective* permeability is of the order of 50 when considering induction by H and Z during the building process. Since the ambient inducing field is reduced within the material by the demagnetising field it follows that a state of equilibrium magnetisation is reached as the *internal* field strength approaches zero. On this basis, and treating solely with the hull effect, ignoring local superstructures some estimates can be made.

(i) *Vertical Magnetisation during Building*—The intensity of magnetisation due to Z induction reaches some 97% of equilibrium magnetisation. When Z changes as the ship moves from one latitude to another about $66\frac{2}{3}$% of the equilibrium magnetisation behaves as 'soft iron' and the remaining $33\frac{1}{3}$% as permanent 'hard iron'.

(ii) *Athwartship Magnetisation during Building*—The intensity of magnetisation due to H induction reaches roughly the same value (95%) of equilibrium magnetisation. When H changes as the ship changes latitude roughly 43% of the equilibrium magnetisation behaves as 'soft iron' and only 6% of it as permanent 'hard iron'.

(iii) *Longitudinal Magnetisation during Building*—The intensity of magnetisation due to H induction reaches only some 55% of equilibrium magnetisation. When H changes as the ship changes latitude between 19% and 26% of the equilibrium magnetisation remains as 'hard iron' and only some 7% acts as 'soft iron'. If the effective permeability is temporarily increased due to vibration and movement in a seaway due to bad weather the longitudinal magnetisation will change appropriately so that if course is now altered, and the permeability does not instantaneously measure up to the value on the previous course some retained longitudinal magnetisation is likely and will cause unwanted deviation. Since longitudinal magnetisation is less stable than athwartship magnetisation these effects are likely to be greater when altering course from north or south towards east or west. Nevertheless, athwartship magnetisation even though more stable is nearer to the compass and could well produce similar type deviation. It remains in doubt which of these effects is the greater, until more information is known from a study of deviation at sea.

Retentive Error

The magnetisation of ships is complex and much work was done in connection with degaussing procedures as an antidote to the magnetic mine. But, in the present context, we are dealing with the *compass position* and the temporary effects which cause unpredictable deviation. Individual masters and officers vouch for its presence within their experience. The writer has no hesitation in appealing to navigators at sea to set the record straight. There is no intention of suggesting that officers have time to waste, but this is a very earnest request for some positive detail which only officers on the bridge can supply should they have a few minutes to spare now and again during the course of their normal bridge duties. Those who might be anxious to participate in filling this gap of information need only to keep their eyes open and have paper and pen at the ready. Although retentive error needs investigating it is sometimes referred to as 'error caused by retained magnetism', 'hysteresis error', or, incorrectly as 'Gaussing error'. To avoid confusion the term *retentive error* alone will be used below.

Observing Retentive Error

Perhaps the principal thing to guard against is to record mistakenly deviations subsequent to alteration of course which are purely deviations due to an incompletely adjusted compass, and not due to retained magnetism at all. Clearly, *uncorrected* deviations must appear after altering course in any event, and these may also be of different value due to change of latitude. It is necessary therefore, when trying to establish retentive error, that some knowledge exists regarding the deviation 'on the new course' when it was *last taken* and as it appears in the deviation journal. If the 'new course' is to be northerly or southerly such deviation may be forecast approximately on the basis that it changes inversely as the earth's horizontal field strength. A deviation which accords with such a value would not suggest the existence of retentive error. If the 'new course' is to be easterly or westerly such forecasts are more difficult unless coefficient B has been carefully corrected to near zero value by the fore and aft magnets and Flinders bar some time previously.

With these thoughts in mind the observer can now be on the look-out for those special occasions when, after a long period on one course, a pronounced alteration of course is made. If substantial deviation appears (5°, 10°, 15° or more— all have been reported from time to time) which quite definitely conflicts with any tentative prediction then it would seem that *retentive error* is present. This is the thing to look for. The theory of retained magnetism as it affects the compass indicates that the retentive error will be *easterly* if the course is altered *anti-clockwise*, i.e. *to port*; it will be *westerly* if the alteration is *clockwise*, i.e. to *starboard*. Other things being equal, theory suggests that an alteration from north or south towards east or west would produce greater retentive error than those occasions when the course is altered from east or west towards north or south. But—and this is important—an observing officer should not be misled by the theoretical guides stated here. The precise *opposite* might occur and it is just because so little real information exists that the truth needs to be known even if careful observations show the complete absence of any evidence of retentive error in particular instances.

Duration of Retentive Error

A further symptom of retentive error is the *duration* of the observed error, and its rate of decay. Any period of time from a few minutes to one or two days have been suggested. It is implied that after an interval retentive error gradually disappears, or changes towards a value (not necessarily anticipated from previous records) which then remains unchanged. The decay of retentive error would seem, by casual reports, to take place usually within the hour after assuming the new course— but there again, no data is available and this is another of the things, probably the most important, which needs to be observed.

The duration of the error is very important also from the navigating point of view because if retentive error of the order of 10° or 15° occurs initially in congested waters it is vital that there should be *no delay* in observing it. A fast ship (temporarily deprived of the gyro compass) navigating in intricate waters needs to know the compass error *immediately* after altering course so that the new course can be pursued with confidence. Thereafter the error must be checked frequently at short intervals to detect quickly any changes taking place so that the ship may be kept constantly on the required true course. Sometimes we hear a familiar exhortation to the officer of the watch to 'take an error in a quarter of an hour or so when the magnetic compass has had time to settle'! This completely misses the point. The time to take the first error observation is *directly* the course has changed, i.e. when retentive error is most likely and at maximum value. Furthermore it is the ship magnetisation which is temporarily unstable (not the compass) and the navigator needs to know the extent of the instability (in terms of the deviation it causes) when it is greatest, that is, just after altering course.

Likely Areas for Retentive Error

The fact that retentive error is possible when a bold alteration has been made from a course which has been held for some time raises the question as to the minimum time required on the 'old course'. Observing officers might consider anything over 24 hours and naturally, the longer the better. One might add that rough weather increases the chances of observing the elusive deviations since this increases the effective permeability upon which the error depends. There are many long sea passages on substantially the same course followed by an alteration of 50° or more when rounding principal headlands like Cape of Good Hope, Cape Leeuwin, and even the South Foreland on a homeward passage from the West Indies. Often an ocean voyage is terminated by a very pronounced alteration of course into harbour at the last minute; such cases provide navigating officers with a splendid opportunity for observing retentive error, provided the chance is not missed in spite of the little time available before picking up the pilot or going into berth.

Recording Retentive Error

The reader now knows what is involved, and if he is interested to participate in confirming or denying the existence of retentive error within his experience he needs to know a simple arrangement for the results of his observations, so that when these are collated with others and examined they may form the basis for conclusions which, it is hoped, can be later promulgated for the benefit of all. Some kind of *pro forma* is desirable. The writer suggests the arrangement which is printed below since it contains the minimum number of significant items.

Record of Retentive Error at the Standard Magnetic Compass

   (i) Name of Ship ....

  (ii) *En route* from .... to ....

 (iii) **True** course prior to bold alteration ....°

 (iv) Time on 'old Course' in (iii) above ....days .... hours

  (v) Weather and sea conditions generally during,

        (*a*) First half of 'old course' ....

        (*b*) Second half of 'old course' ....

 (vi) Average variation and deviation during,

        (*a*) First half of 'old course' (Var'n............ Dev............)

        (*b*) Second half of 'old course' (Var'n............ Dev............)

 (vii) Deviation immediately **before** alteration of course (Comp. Co......Dev......)

(viii) Deviation immediately **after** alteration of course (Comp. Co......Dev......)

 (ix) Deviation subsequently, after:

        (*a*) Five minutes   (Comp. Co......... Dev.........)

        (*b*) Ten minutes   (Comp. Co......... Dev.........)

        (*c*) Fifteen minutes   (Comp. Co......... Dev.........)

        (*d*) Twenty minutes   (Comp. Co......... Dev.........)

        (*e*) One hour   (Comp. Co......... Dev.........)

        (*f*) Twelve hours   (Comp. Co......... Dev.........)*

        (*g*) Twenty-four hours (Comp. Co......... Dev.........)*

    (* To be recorded if the 'new course' is maintained for a sufficiently long period of time.)

   (x) **Remarks:** The observer's name, the time and date of observation, the locality of the observation/s and any further significant information he may care to give.

Submissions

It is understood and well appreciated that in these days the navigator is principally concerned with his gyro compass, particularly in coastal waters. To ask him to take special note of the magnetic compass at a time when he may be otherwise occupied would be presumptuous. The intention is solely to solicit his help in providing information which may eventually help others who, through an electrical or mechanical failure, are deprived temporarily of the services of the gyro. These failures do occur and more needs to be known about retentive error to safeguard the course when bold alterations of course need to be taken. Of course, a small amount of information is not useless. In this sense—'anything is better than nothing', but complete records of instances are best of all. The appeal is therefore open to any who are interested and tempted to take part.

A Caution

Any ship's officer who obtains information of this kind should only record what he has personally seen and observed for himself. It may be tempting, sometimes, to quote second-hand from an associate who 'remembers' that, 'when I was on such and such a ship we had 17° of deviation turning into so and so after a passage across the Pacific'. No doubt he did, but the search is for specific instances recorded at the time, and not reported cases where the detail is largely missing or just a memory trace of the past, however interesting.

A Safe Course—Everyone's Concern

Whilst the subject of this invitation to contribute information on retentive error is long overdue it remains just as important as it has always been, and for so long as the magnetic compass remains aboard ship as the stand-by against a gyro failure. Since everyone from Cadet Officer to Master is involved compass-wise aboard ship it seems appropriate that they should also be wise about their compass if they intend to promote safety at sea by heading in the right direction!

CHAPTER 10

Magnetic Correctors - Effects and Interactions in Practice.

PART of the mystery which attaches to magnetic compass compensation lies in the theoretical extent to which the practitioner is taken while learning the subject. Whilst a considerable knowledge is required to pass an examination much of the detail acquired is not used in practice. In a sense too much knowledge can have the opposite of the desired effect; real situations become over-complicated and the navigator is discouraged from attempting a more tentative approach to some real and genuine adjustments. Similar observations can no doubt be made about other professions where a wealth of detail is necessary to form the foundations of the occupation but once mastered is, in the event, substituted with the everyday expertise developed from continual contact in the field.

Certainly it is true that a little knowledge can be embarrassing, and too much can be frightening. It seems a good idea to provide the navigator, who wishes to interest himself further with his standard magnetic compass, with some of the kinds of information he needs most and can rarely find in books and which is, furthermore, often omitted from his detailed studies. This information, to be most useful, should deal with the effects which the several correctors have on the compass as well as the effects which they may have on each other. Anyone, standing by the binnacle, might justifiably wonder to what extent the sphere correctors eliminate coefficient D when placed mid-way on their brackets and what might then be the effect in actual values of moving them to the extremities of the brackets, or even removing one temporarily. One might reasonably wonder what correction for induced B is afforded by a 12-inch length of Flinders bar in a given latitude and what might happen if this were reduced to six inches. Examination of the heeling error magnets in the retaining bucket may cause one to speculate upon their effect in real terms at the compass itself, and whether any side effects might occur if they are raised, lowered, altered in number, or even reversed.

The answers to some or all of these must surely be useful to anyone contemplating minor adjustments aboard ship to their standard compass because they create a realistic sense of awareness of what is going on each time a particular corrector is moved.

The Order of Precedence

It does not come amiss, before considering individual effects, to recapitulate briefly the order in which basic corrections should be done, so that, should one corrector interact upon another, the adjustments made to any one correction does not upset something previously concluded.

Fundamentally, soft iron (highly permeable) correctors must precede hard iron (low permeability) correctors. This is not, apart from one exception, due to interaction between the several correctors but rather to the fact that some correctors produce unwanted effects beyond their designed function.

The precise sequence of placing the several correctors is as follows:

First; soft iron correctors—of these,

  (*a*) Flinders bar precedes,

  (*b*) Soft iron spheres.

Second; permanent correctors—of these,

  (*c*) Heeling error correctors precede,

  (*d*) Horizontal magnets.

The Reasons

The sequence is stated; it needs to be established why this is the preferred order. If one accepts, for the moment, the priority of soft iron correctors over hard iron correctors attention may be directed to each of the former. The Flinders bar needs to precede the spheres simply because the finite cross-section of the bar exhibits $+a$ and $-e$ effects supporting unwanted D of positive sign. Clearly, the spheres which follow need to sweep up this unwanted deviation along with the positive D of the ship. The officer aboard ship or the professional adjuster has, in the event, little to worry about on this score because (with the exception of a new ship) both the Flinders bar and the sphere correctors will be already tentatively in position. Nevertheless, if it is the intention to alter the length of the bar this adjustment should always precede any adjustment of the spheres. Likewise, at a later date, it may become essential (indeed, *should* become essential) to change the length of the Flinders bar, in which event, for the reasons stated, the spheres must be readjusted to accommodate the change in coefficient D; *see* Fig. 19 below.

Turning to the permanent correctors, those used to correct inclination errors head the list. The reason here is that these magnets, placed vertically below the compass, inevitably interact with the soft iron correctors, particularly the Flinders bar. Lengthwise components of induction in the bar establish superimposed fixed quantity poles (for given arrangements of heeling error magnets and length of bar) in the Flinders bar which give rise to some value of coefficient B (force P). It follows therefore, that both the Flinders bar and the heeling error magnets must be in position previously to placing or adjusting the fore and aft horizontal magnets correcting coefficient B. Furthermore, each time that either the Flinders bar or the heeling error magnets need to be adjusted then a check should be made on the correction of coefficient B because either of the former corrections cannot be altered without affecting coefficient B. These points now confirm the necessity for preserving the stated order of precedence. Since the last correctors to be placed or adjusted are the horizontal magnets the navigator has a choice between the fore and aft magnets and the athwartships magnets. He may choose whichever set is the more convenient though it is sometimes recommended that whichever is the larger of coefficients B and C (although in practice this will usually remain unknown till the event) should be adjusted first.

Practice and Theory

Naturally, it would be pointless to claim that no one needs to study the theory of compass compensation to be proficient in the art though it is very true to say that, paradoxically, there are thousands who have studied the theory and are not in the least practised in the art of compass adjustment—probably due to lack of opportunity and necessity—but that is another story. Certainly every qualified officer for a Master's F/G certificate has studied the subject, among others, and been pronounced competent—at least that's what it says on the certificate. To attain this he will have practised hundreds of calculations of one sort or another in order to demonstrate his knowledge of

D

the behaviour of deviation at a compass under varying conditions of course, heel, geographic location and the like. He will have made quantitative estimates of deviations likely to occur under different conditions and made further calculations designed to inform him to what new adjusted distances from the compass correctors of one kind or another need to be reset. Most of these—not all—are useful exercises to demonstrate an *understanding* of the subject but are substantially useless in practice. The main reason why much of the quantitative work serves little purpose aboard ship is because there is no need to calculate likely deviations when these have been observed and recorded and only need eliminating! What is needed is a working appreciation of the individual correctors and what may be expected of them when they are physically handled. Excepting for the moment calculations which relate to an analysis of deviation and those used to separate the parts of coefficients B the rest are interesting but contribute little to practical adjustment.

Before considering several individual effects it is fairly obvious that it would be impossible to provide the navigator with compehensive data on all the possible arrangements of correctors attached to binnacles of different types, compasses of various strengths and design, and correctors of different numbers and sizes. There is, of course, no need anyway, because, as has been pointed out, deviation can be observed and removed. The following details are therefore submitted as being representative to throw some light on much of what usually remains hidden or speculative. The examples described below may be taken as typical for an Admiralty Pattern AP1950 compass housed in a conventional binnacle or a commercial liquid compass of magnetic moment approximately 1600 cgs units. The ambient field due to the earth for each of the examples listed is appropriate to London, viz. H = 0·184 and Z = 0·450 oersteds.

Horizontal Magnets

Figure 16 illustrates graphically the order of corrective deviation provided by an assembly of two 9-in. × $\frac{3}{8}$-in. fore and aft corrector magnets each located at the same stated distances below the compass. The form of the curve supports the fact that tan $\delta° \propto 1/d^3$ where d represents successive distances at which the correctors were placed with the ship initially heading 090°/270°(M). Clearly, the behaviour of athwartships magnets is similar, supports the theory used for magnets placed beyond the minimum stipulated distances and agrees with the theoretical methods usually adopted in simple calculations where by $\delta° \propto 1/d^3$ provided that deviations not in excess of about 15°

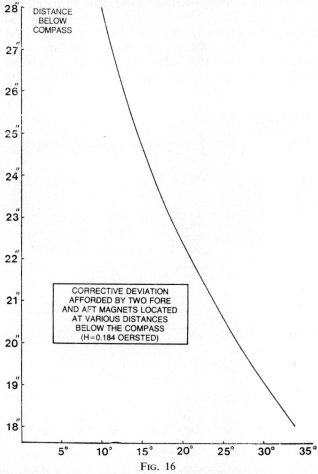

FIG. 16

are considered. Whenever possible a larger number of correctors placed lower in the binnacle is more desirable than to economise on their number and place them higher. A more uniform correcting field at the compass position will thus be ensured. Fig. 16 produces no surprises and demonstrates by observation what was to be expected.

The Soft Iron Sphere Correctors

Figure 17 illustrates graphically the compensating effect, in terms of coefficient D, caused by a single sphere and a symmetrical arrangement of one sphere on each side of the compass. The spheres used are solid 5 in. in diameter. The curves for each sphere individually are not precisely identical even though tests for retentive magnetism confirmed that none was present. Nevertheless, the curves indicate reasonable agreement and show that when the spheres are placed symmetrically each side of the compass the effect of the two

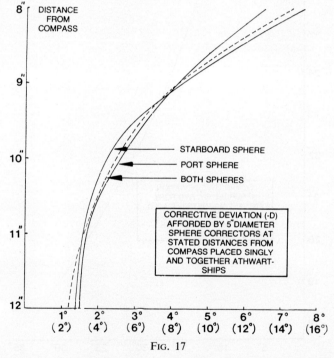

FIG. 17

together, in the case chosen, is twice the effect of a single sphere. The intermittent curve for the two spheres is drawn against a halved scale for deviation to emphasise this point. Although protracted experiments were not performed with a selection of spheres of different sizes it seems that the sometimes quoted rule that two spheres caused 20/11ths of the D compensation afforded by a single sphere is not entirely justified. This is only a small point and it appears quite safe to assume, as a general rule, the obvious conclusion that one sphere at a given distance gives half the correction provided by a pair symmetrically placed.

One of the interesting facts which emerges from a study of the curves shown in Fig. 17 is that the numerical relationship between the amount of D compensation provided and the distance at which spheres are located on the brackets is of the form $\delta° \propto 1/d^4$ and not $\delta° \propto 1/d^3$ as is usually supposed. This discrepancy may be accounted for by the fact that the strengths of the di-poles representing the magnetisation of the spheres is not solely dependent upon induction derived from H alone but partly due to induction arising from the needles or magnetic element of the compass itself. This is a detail which need not concern the practitioner, nor indeed the qualifying officer. The former will have no need for making quantitative estimates because he deals with the deviation as he sees it, whilst the latter may still perform his calculations for examination purposes using $\delta° \propto 1/d^3$ knowing that, although not entirely accurate, assessments made in this way produce acceptable results. The point is made to demonstrate that practice and theory don't always agree unless the theory is complete.

The Flinders Bar

So much has been written about the Flinders bar that a little more won't hurt. To start with, the writer would like to take issue with many qualifying officers who insist on using the lower case 'f' for Flinders. Might it not be better to use a capital 'F' in recognition of Captain Mathew Flinders R.N. after whom the corrector derives its name? The name, by the way, is Flinders and not Flinder; so it seems appropriate to omit all apostrophes both before and after the 's'. If an examiner is at all sensitive, and many of them are, he would tend to be displeased with a qualifying officer who might unintentionally discredit the name of such an eminent explorer.

Figure 18 shows graphically the amount of corrective induced B coefficient caused by the Flinders bar of various lengths in the relatively high Z value of London. Stripped of all other correctors around the binnacle it is seen that for all but the shortest and longest lengths of the bar the correction afforded is almost linearly proportional to the length of the bar. It is not an accurate guide but it is better than nothing and preferable to having just no clue at all. The correction afforded would be greater in still higher latitudes and less in lower latitudes, naturally. In this sense speculation often exists regarding the initial placing of a suitable length and the magical supposed value for induced B is often quoted as between 3° and 5°—but where? In London, Capetown, New York or Tokyo? And does it matter? The answer is—not in the least, so those who like 3°, 4° or 5° may retain their wish well knowing that the estimate doesn't matter until the true value has later been established—but that's another question.

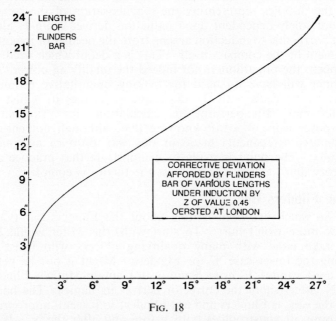

FIG. 18

Very short lengths of Flinders bar are largely ineffective as can be seen. Certainly the 1/12th rule (M Notice 616/72, Appendix 1, paragraph 28) is ill-advised for the shorter lengths. These, to be at all effective, should have the top located *below* the level of the compass element, and not above it. Fig. 18 indicates, also, that when near maximum lengths are used the correction provided is very substantial and it appears that even if lengths in excess of 24 in. were possible little further correction would be gained. From the form of the graph it appears that little more is to be expected from exceeding the normally designed maximum length of 24 in. Although Fig. 18 is drawn in terms of deviation to provide a practical appreciation of what is happening, the reader, who may be familiar with more of the detail of the subject, will recognise the advantage to be gained by plotting the constant 'c' against length and subsequently interpreting the deviation from $\sin B = cZ/\lambda H$ for any geographical location.

The D of the Flinders Bar

It is surprising how few navigators have ever held a piece of Flinders bar in their hands. Even the modest sections are quite heavy. A 12-in. length, if accidentally dropped, can cause damage to a wooden deck or severe injury to the toes. A qualify officer at examination time does well to handle only the smaller pieces from choice and so avoid wrecking the examiner's domain as well as his own reputation. Clearly, such a corrector of considerable mass and high permeability causes several magnetic effects (a, e and k among them) additional to its designed purpose (c). Perhaps the most prominent are a and e which, with the Flinders bar conventionally forward of the compass imposes an unwanted D of positive sign. It has already been mentioned above that it is for this reason that the sphere correctors need to follow and not precede the placing of the Flinders bar. This unwanted D is shown in Fig. 19. The graph reveals several items of practical importance. First of all the incidence of this coefficient in the first place— particularly to the unsuspecting. Secondly, the fact that different *lengths* of bar cause different values for D; a point which can be easily overlooked. A study of the graph shows that $D° \propto \sqrt{l}$ where l is the length of the bar shipped. Whilst the graph speaks for itself, the navigator, who is rightly exhorted to eliminate induced B whenever he discovers it (going round the Cape, etc.), should not overlook the fact that when he does this with either a shorter or longer Flinders bar the D compensation has changed slightly in consequence. This should not be a cause of consternation but rather an appreciation of the sense of the likely change which may occur in the most embarrassing coefficient of all, i.e. D. With the spheres already shipped athwartships a substantial *lengthening* of the bar should be accompanied by a fractional half inch, or so) movement of each sphere *towards the compass*; if the bar is *shortened* the spheres are moved *outwards*. The numerical relationship of $D° \propto \sqrt{l}$ need not worry the man on the bridge, but the fact that he is aware of what happens distinguished him from those who pretend. At least he will

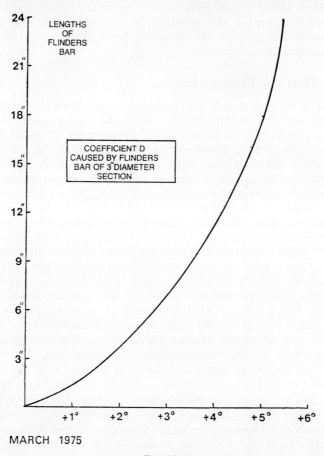

COEFFICIENT D
CAUSED BY FLINDERS
BAR OF 3″DIAMETER
SECTION

LENGTHS
OF
FLINDERS
BAR

MARCH 1975

FIG. 19

perform a tentative readjustment of the spheres, slight though it is, for the best of reasons, namely, practical ones.

Heeling Error Correctors

Ships built in Europe, North America and Japan form a large proportion of the world's tonnage and, because of this, the majority of ships have, at their standard compass, an assembly of vertical corrector magnets with north seeking ends uppermost. A collection of 3, 5, or even 7 magnets in the retaining bucket is not unusual. Most qualified navigators recognise these as inclination error correctors. They contribute more to creating a *steady compass* than any other corrector but they suffer the disadvantage of doing so in one given latitude only unless they are readjusted from time to time. Much has been written in these pages of how this should be done—how little trouble it is to secure a steady compass on courses near to 000°/180° when rolling in a seaway—how little time it takes, and so on. But words won't alter things, and there are still too many aboard ship who are reluctant or too timid to try. They need to be driven to the binnacle at gunpoint. Meantime a transmitting compass faithfully transmits every oscillation of a neglected compass. Such is the way of things.

Figure 20 shows, simply, the corrective deviation provided by a typical array of vertical correctors. The two obvious results are illustrated; the effect of raising or lowering the

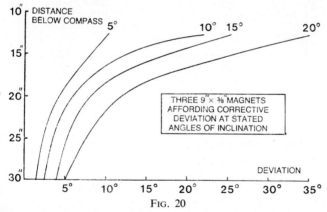

FIG. 20

bucket and the effect which increasing the heel has on the deviating component. Since ships—except a few sailing vessels heeled steadily to the wind—do not suffer heeling error as such, the effect of increasing the heel is clearly interpreted as a function of the unsteadiness produced under rolling and/or pitching conditions. Quantitative assessments for heeling error as featured in examinations are usually quite pointless from the practical aspect, but since they need to be done the reader's attention is drawn to Fig. 20 which shows quite clearly, in this instance, that inclination errors are *not* directly proportional to the actual heel as it usually supposed, nor even proportional to its sine ratio. The addition of Fig. 21 further demonstrates that a near linear relationship only exists when the corrector magnets are near the bottom of the tube.

These details, important as they are, need not worry the navigator aboard if he adopts a *practical* and tentative approach which means literally removing any unsteadiness appearing when the ship rolls and pitches in a seaway. Of what earthly

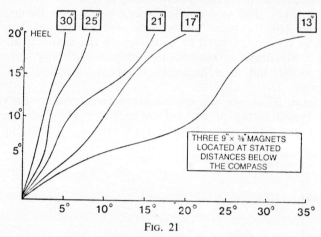

FIG. 21

use is an academic appreciation of the effect of disturbing force vectors, however interesting, if they are allowed to persist so that the card oscillates 10° or 15° each side of the lubber mark? The graphs are there for perusal—don't discard them as useless—study them—understand what they mean and the inference to be drawn from them and then *do something, right away*; move the bucket up or down and see what happens—the chances are that you will gain a perfectly steady compass within 10 minutes! But you won't, will you? You'll put the book down, or throw it on a pile of other casual and discarded literature and claim you have more important things to do (what, for instance?)—and you'll have an uncomfortable feeling that somehow you nearly became involved in something you'd rather avoid, till sloth, or fear, or both won the day! Yes?

Heeling Error Correctors and the Flinders Bar

From what has been stated above there is an obligation to maintain the correction for inclination errors with changes of latitude. There is also an obligation to adjust the length of the Flinders Bar to remove the likely growth of deviation on courses near to 090°/270° when a ship penetrates the opposite hemisphere. Interaction between the two correctors is, therefore, to be anticipated. Fig. 22 shows the effects to be expected with the group of correctors chosen. The points to look for

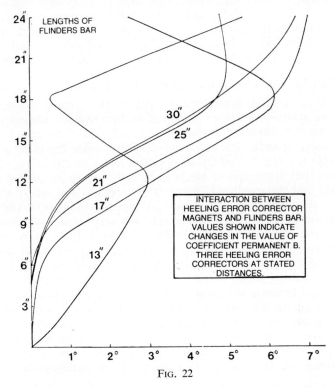

FIG. 22

are as follows. Firstly, the unwanted side effect is a change of *permanent* B coefficient each time either the length of bar, or the number and positions of vertical magnets is changed. Secondly, the fact that the permanent coefficient can change by up to 7° or more is not insignificant. Thirdly, as expected, the longer lengths of Flinders bar have the greater effects and lastly, the rather unpredictable effects which occur when the vertical correctors are raised towards the top of the tube. Dealing with the last first, it seems that whenever possible more correctors mid-way in the tube are more desirable than a smaller number near the top. In general the side effect is fairly linear for lengths of bar which are not extreme and heights of magnets which fall short of the highest position in the tube.

The values of coefficient B are quite appreciable when caused by these interacting correctors, but once again, the practitioner needs only to recognise what is happening and act sensibly. Once a reasonable correction for induced B has been achieved then, whenever heeling error is recorrected, the deviation on 090°/270° should be checked and the fore and aft magnets adjusted slightly to eliminate the *change which appears*.

Heeling Error Correctors and the Spheres

The same kind of interaction between the vertical magnets and the sphere correctors is bound to be present. Owing to the normal positioning of the spheres each side of the compass the effects of induction cause no deviation since the effect on one side is counteracted by an opposite effect on the other. It follows that if one sphere needs to be removed an imbalance is created and the residual Q force, of one sign or the other, will affect the deviation on headings approaching 000°/180°. Experiments show that these effects are very small and, once again, the navigator aboard ship need have little to worry about except, perhaps, to remember that a symmetrical distribution of a pair of smaller spheres is preferable—if they were available—which is unlikely. This form of interaction is very slight because the lengthwise components of induction in the case of the Flinders bar now take the form of cross-wise components which are far less damaging. Theory demands an understanding of what *can* happen; practice shows what *does* happen—always, the one needs the other unless one is content to blunder around and let the compass point indifferently.

Practical Awareness

If you have read thus far, perhaps it is because you are interested, or you wanted to see what happens next. This depends so much on who you are: the casually interested; the keen enthusiast; the armchair navigator who knows it all anyway; the qualifying officer who needs to know it eventually; or, the master aboard ship who is inflicted with each and has to put up with them all. Essentially, the foregoing notes and illustrations are intended solely for those who either already do, or intend to, *apply* whatever theoretical knowledge they have to *practical use at their compass.* Since the examples illustrated deal with typical effects under likely conditions they serve the purpose of creating or improving a sense of practical awareness. Suspicions are removed and substituted with greater certainty each time a corrector is adjusted. Correctors are related to the deviations they cause, and there are no sums to do. It is hoped that the paraphernalia in and surrounding the binnacle may now have greater significance for those who are not afraid to practice what, at some time or other, they have been taught. After all, safety at sea stems directly from a measure of *competence*, and that is the compelling word on each certificate we all carry—the competence of the officer on the bridge, at sea, to exercise some degree of compass wisdom along with many other things he seems to do so much better.

CHAPTER 11

The Multi - Purpose Sphere Corrector.

ANYONE aboard ship, faced with a gyro failure and having to use the magnetic compass, is often irritated at the outset when removing the canvas cover over the binnacle. The thing seldom comes off easily, even when the lashings are loosened, because the brackets supporting the sphere correctors catch up in the bights and folds of canvas. Even when the cover is off the contemporary navigator doesn't view the prospect of using the magnetic compass with any great relish, still less pleasure. He feels that the gyro should not have let him down; or make him dependent upon such an apparently archaic instrument for heading reference and general navigation. He even looks at the binnacle with displeasure and some mistrust. Yet a new binnacle, recently delivered from the compass-shop, is not all that unattractive. One not so new which has been hiding under the cover for a while does seem a little uninspiring. Certainly the shape is familiar and characteristic. It is dominated by the Flinders bar case on the fore side and the very substantial brackets supporting the sphere correctors on each side. It is the spheres that are to claim our attention because, although covered with indifferent paint (bless the man who had the courage to paint the port sphere red and the starboard sphere green—just for fun) they conceal a fascinating story of hidden influence, of concealed magnetic ingenuity, and several surprises. The casual enquirer is usually told that the spheres are 'soft iron correctors' or, 'quadrantal correctors'—but sometimes professional navigators describe them crudely, which only reflects their lack of sensitivity, particularly those who go further and identify ownership—this is indelicate to say the least; certainly disrespectful. The proper terms to use are 'sphere corrector', 'soft iron spheres', 'spherical quadrantal correctors', etc.

Le Raison d'etre

If the professional is asked by the officer cadet or other curious bystander the reason for the sphere correctors, the short answer is 'to correct quadrantal deviation'; the matter is then usually dropped. This is not surprising because of all the correctors on or within the confines of the binnacle none is so interesting and capable of so many beneficial effects as the sphere correctors. For those who have hitherto studied the subject much may have been missed. For the uninitiated much needs to be known, or at least appreciated. For both, the story of the spheres should intrigue. Occasionally, during the following discussion, the official notation of the subject is used—the more expert will recognise the references, but for those less skilled the invitation is open to become more acquainted and, it is hoped, interested in the process.

First of all one must accept that almost invariably part of the total deviation pattern at a magnetic compass position is quadrantal. Analysis reveals that this is most likely the approximate coefficient D of positive sign; a type of deviation which displays its maximum value on the intercardinal headings, is usually westerly in the NW and SE quadrants, easterly in the NE and SW quadrants and zero on each of the cardinal headings. What could be more embarrassing? Of the several deviation patterns which form the resultant curve none offers a greater nuisance than coefficient D. One does not need to be a very skilled navigator to recognise the implication of, for instance, a value of $4°$ for coefficient D. When the ship swings from one intercardinal heading to the next the *change of deviation* is no less than $8°$! Invariably the swing of the needle is double the value of the coefficient. Coefficient D of the order of $6°$, $7°$, or $8°$ (quite usual aboard ship) produce *changes* of $12°$, $14°$ or $16°$ over a $90°$ swing of the ship's head by compass! No one doubts the inconvenience and embarrassment which such deviation causes and the necessity for eliminating it in pursuit of safe navigation.

Conditions for D to be Zero

Although the presence of the type of deviation mentioned has been stated there is a further point of appreciation required at this stage. In isolation the positive D is caused by the earth's H induction into the high permeability (soft iron) proportion of symmetrically distributed horizontal iron. A casual thought about a ship's structure with reference to any reasonable compass position confirms that such structure extends continuously forward and aft $(-a)$ and continuously across the ship $(-e)$. Both effects cause coefficient D; the former negative and the latter positive. Magnetically $-e$ exceeds $-a$ simply because of the proximity of the ship's sides. For this reason coefficient D is invariably positive but it is important to consider the ship to exhibit both signs of D with the positive sign predominating. If this is borne carefully in mind it is not difficult to accept that so far as D is concerned the continuity of fore and aft iron $(-a)$ automatically eliminates an equivalent amount of transverse iron $(-e)$ so that the predominating effect of the latter *alone* needs to be eliminated to reduce D to zero. When this is done the residual $+D = -D$, i.e. it has disappeared, or for those who are more familiar with the theory, $D = O$ when $-a_2 = -e_2$.

Effect on the Directing Field Northward

The importance of the point just made lies in the fact that, unlike the correction of some other coefficients where the disturbing component of field strength is reduced to zero as, for instance, in the case of P causing coefficient B, when dealing with D the coefficient is reduced to zero in a manner which leaves a large proportion of ferro-magnetic material magnetised even though deviation can no longer occur. One might be tempted to say—'Well, the deviation is zero and therefore there is no further need for concern, surely?' Unfortunately, the continuity of both fore and aft and athwartships structure which remains reduces the mean field strength northward at the compass position. Of and by itself this is most unfortunate because although the embarrassment of quadrantal deviation is removed the field strength at the compass position must not be allowed to fall to a level below about 50% of the ambient H else the compass will not function! It may be demonstrated that the causes of D alone (a and e) affect the mean directing field at the compass; none of the causes of other coefficients have this effect. Furthermore, the effect on the mean field strength is always adverse. Whatever means are proposed for the correction of coefficient D they should include an effect which restores at least some of the lost field strength at the compass position. To these ends the pioneer scientists like Lord Kelvin, Archibald Smith and others directed their earnest attention and devised the spherical-shaped corrector which has become so much part of the bridge scene.

Quadrantal Correctors

Clearly, if the causes of coefficient D are the effects of H

induction into fore and aft and transverse soft iron, taken out of context, then it would seem reasonable that small rods of highly-permeable iron alloys might be used as correctors if placed near to the compass. This, of course, is true and several types of quadrantal corrector have been used in the past, such as soft iron bars, boxes of chain, and soft iron cylinders with hemi-spherical ends. Most were originally found unsatisfactory because the correcting field was not sufficiently uniform over the area swept out by the compass needle system, particularly in the days before short multiple needle arrangements were demanded by later theoretical considerations. With large compass needles octantal deviations were likely to occur. Furthermore, corrections effected in one latitude were not maintained in other latitudes owing to excessive interaction between the compass needles and the soft iron correctors. These deficiencies led to the spherical corrector which possesses several advantages over other types.

Sphere Type Correctors

One of the special features attached to a spherical corrector is that when uniformly magnetised it exhibits a field which corresponds closely with that of a very small imaginary magnet at its centre. This has the effect of permitting the corrector to be placed comparatively near to the compass (which is convenient) while retaining the advantages of a greater *relative* distance which is magnetically desirable. In the event it is useful to consider the magnetised sphere in plan view showing a double di-pole at its centre; one supporting a fore and aft di-pole ($-a_1$) and the other a transverse di-pole ($+e_1$). It may be shown, and many readers will have already established the fact for themselves, that the latter produces a magnetic field twice the value of the former owing to what are popularly referred to as 'end-on' and 'broadside' effects.

When sphere correctors are placed on brackets athwart the compass the excess of the ship's $-e$ over $-a$ is reduced to zero by the simultaneous effects of $+e_1$ and $-a_1$, both of which superimpose a D coefficient of negative sign. Clearly, the separately resolved effects are in the ratio of two to one, so that two-thirds of the offending D is eliminated by $+e_1$ of the spheres and one-third by the $-a_1$ component. Fig. 23 shows in some detail the causes of coefficient D, including that of the Flinders bar q.v., and the manner in which the spheres ensure that $-a_2 = -e_2$ with D reduced to zero.

The Effect of the Spheres on the Mean Field Strength

The discussion so far is necessary in order to point out the secondary advantage of the sphere type corrector. The continuous feature of $-a_1$ is not helpful in restoring the mean

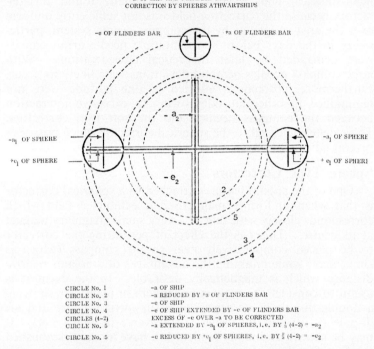

<table>
<tr><td>CIRCLE No. 1</td><td>-a OF SHIP</td></tr>
<tr><td>CIRCLE No. 2</td><td>-a REDUCED BY +a OF FLINDERS BAR</td></tr>
<tr><td>CIRCLE No. 3</td><td>-e OF SHIP</td></tr>
<tr><td>CIRCLE No. 4</td><td>-e OF SHIP EXTENDED BY -e OF FLINDERS BAR</td></tr>
<tr><td>CIRCLES (4-2)</td><td>EXCESS OF -e OVER -a TO BE CORRECTED</td></tr>
<tr><td>CIRCLE No. 5</td><td>-a EXTENDED BY $-a_1$ OF SPHERES, i.e. BY $\frac{1}{5}$ (4-2) = $-a_2$</td></tr>
<tr><td>CIRCLE No. 5</td><td>-e REDUCED BY $+e_1$ OF SPHERES, i.e. BY $\frac{2}{5}$ (4-2) = $-e_2$</td></tr>
</table>

Fig. 23

field strength at the compass; in fact it imposes a further reduction. On the other hand $+e_1$ causes an increase in the mean field strength and because numerically $+e_1 = {}_2(-a_1)$ there is an overall improvement in the mean field northward caused by the sphere correctors. Since, however, both $-a_2$ and $-e_2$ still remain after D has been corrected the mean field northward cannot be restored completely to the undiluted ambient field H but there is nevertheless a definite improvement once the spheres are properly shipped. In this rather special way the spheres, (i) eliminate coefficient D and, (ii) partially restore the mean field strength northward.

The Side Effect of the Flinders Bar

If compass Doctors diagnose magnetic illnesses and prescribe the remedies it would not be surprising to anticipate possible side effects from time to time. A case in point is the Flinders bar which, apart from fulfilling its designed purpose of eliminating cZ, is also induced by H and features a $+a$ and $-e$ effects. These naturally contribute to a positive D coefficient indicating clearly that the bar should be in position before shipping the spheres. In this sense the side effect of the Flinders bar is adverse. In fact the D effect of the Flinders bar is governed to some extent by its length; values of 2° for a 6-in. length, 4° for 12 in., and 6° for 24 in. are not uncommon! With such amounts being functions of length the navigator should remember that when adjusting the length of the Flinders bar in the matter of coefficient B he should not overlook the change likely to occur in coefficient D, take the opportunity of checking the D correction and make adjustments to the position of the spheres if necessary. This is a very practical point which has so far eluded the examining authority who are most anxious that practising navigators should adjust the Flinders bar when necessary. This serious side effect should not be overlooked. Nevertheless, on the basis of what has already been said of the spheres the reader can hardly fail to recognise the advantage which the Flinders bar bestowes by increasing the mean field northward. Since its $+a$ contributes to the mean field while its $-e$ reduces it, first thoughts indicate that no benefit accrues. The former, however, is numerically twice as much as the latter and demonstrates once more the beneficial effect of any form of soft iron corrector placed within the horizontal plane through the compass and close to it.

The Peichl Grid

With the strength of the mean field northward in mind the ingenuity displayed by fitting what might be called the Peichl Grid is a further example of an erstwhile quadrantal corrector of unusual design. Two elliptical brass rings were fitted around the compass in a plane parallel to the deck. Their major axis lay athwartships. The two rings supported a series of high permeability rods which radiated from the centre of the compass like the spokes of a wheel. The difference between the two coincident major axes of the rings was made to be greater than the difference between the two coincident minor axes. The grid therefore supported shorter rods nearer to the fore and line and longer rods closer to the athwartships line. The former are recognised as $+a$ effects and the latter as $+e$ effects. Since $+e$ exceeds $+a$ the system acted as a quadrantal corrector for $+D$. The basic reason for the design, however, was to increase the mean field northward which the arrangement of $+a$ and $+e$ does admirably. Although the system described dates back to submarine compasses of World War I, a similar type of corrector though much smaller but based on the same principle, was used during World War II within tanks and other military vehicles. Such illustrations are mentioned to emphasise how important it is to ensure that quadrantal correctors, whatever the type, not only eliminate D but help to restore the field strength at the position occupied by the compass.

More Quadrantal Deviation

The requirements of a well-placed compass are generally known; placed on the fore and aft centre-line with local structure as symmetrically disposed as possible. Occasionally this cannot be entirely achieved with the result that additional unwanted deviation appears and needs special attention. A case in point is coefficient E (b and d effects of equal amount and same sign) which creates a secondary pattern of quadrantal deviation combining with D to distort the curve both in position and amplitude by the respective signs and amounts of D and E. Officers who are familiar with the theory of deviation know what is involved and the detailed steps necessary to deal with the intrusion of coefficient E. To those unfamiliar all that needs to be said is that the sphere correctors effect a correction of this coefficient with no more trouble than that required for D except that to eliminate E alone the spheres need to be orientated at $45°$ to the fore and aft line. As would be expected, at a badly placed compass, *both* D and E would have values. The D would be positive and the E of either one sign or the other depending upon the asymmetry of iron material surrounding the compass. In this event the spheres must be made to occupy some position which is neither athwartships, fore and aft, nor at $45°$ to the fore and aft line, i.e. they must be 'slewed' to some intermediate position which can be computed once the individual values of D and E are known. This rarely happens because care is taken to site the compass properly. Few navigators have ever seen the spheres in position other than on each side of the compass but the point is made so that one is aware that the spheres can perform this additional service should the need arise. To this point of the discussion the sphere correctors eliminate D, coefficient E if need be, and help to restore the mean field strength northward. For those familiar with the accepted notation of the subject these functions embrace the parameters a, e, b, d and of course λ_2. If this seems an acceptable credit balance thus far; more is to come!

Inclination Error—The Effect of the Spheres

If the extent to which the magnetic field at a compass is deviated can be analysed into the separate effects of various constants when the ship is upright it seems reasonable to expect that when the ship is either listed or trimmed that further components of magnetic field disturbance are likely to occur and would require similar study and investigation. Since the deck is no longer horizontal the frame of reference has changed and the subject can become complex. Since ships do not (if it can be helped) navigate with a permanent list there is little point to such an investigation to cover the heeled or pitched condition solely to understand the cause and subsequent behaviour of deviation. Nevertheless, ships at sea roll and pitch and more often than not do both together. Consequently, additional parameters, if allowed to do so, will produce an *unsteady compass* in a seaway. This is, of course, most undesirable and efforts are made aboard ship to 'correct heeling error' to prevent this trouble. Several routines are available for doing this though it invariably entails introducing one or more corrector magnets vertically below the compass. For reasons that need not be explained here it must be mentioned that if the correct procedures are followed a simultaneous correction for the effects of both roll and pitch can be achieved with a single effort; in other words 'inclination errors' are eliminated and a steady compass is restored.

Although not specifically designed as heeling error correctors the soft iron spheres generally mitigate some of the causes of heeling error. In this sense the sphere can be usefully resolved into $-k_1$ as well as $+e_1$ and $-a_1$ already referred to. Bearing in mind that after the removal of D there remains $-e_2$ and $-a_2$ of equal amount both of these soft iron effects are induced by Z the moment the ship rolls and pitches respectively. It follows that $+e_1$ when the ship rolls ($-a_1$ when the ship pitches) and $-k_1$ when the ship both rolls and pitches are induced similarly by Z in the same sense to reduce the heeling

error effects of the ship ($+kZ$ and $-eZ$). It cannot be denied
that $-a_1$ of the spheres has a slightly adverse effect in this
connection but the two points in favour demonstrate clearly
that when the spheres are shipped in position each side of the
compass they help, on balance, to produce a steadier compass
when the ship is moving in a seaway.

A further point arises in the matter of $-k_1$ of the spheres.
Clearly, the spherical shape of the quandrantal corrector was
designed partly with this in mind since the ship effect is
invariably of opposite sign ($+k$). If this is fully recognised
the opportunity of building up the value of $-k_1$ still further,
until it slightly exceeds the corresponding $+k$ of the ship, will

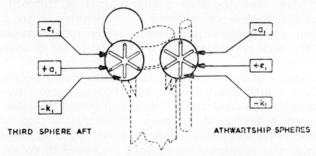

THIRD SPHERE AFT   ATHWARTSHIP SPHERES

Fig. 24

provide a means of correcting inclination errors aboard ship
which is *maintained over a wide range of latitude*! By this
mean R is reduced to zero with a vertical magnet and $-a_2$,
$-e_2$ and $-k_2$ are all made equal, which is one of the fundamental requirements to fulfill the 'conditions for no deviation'
at a magnetic compass.   The fitting of a third sphere corrector
aft of the compass is a means of accomplishing this useful
result (p. 373 of *The Ship's Compass*, 2nd Edition, 1970
explains the detail of such procedure).   The only other alternative is to provide the means for raising or lowering the Flinders
bar so that the requisite corrective values of cZ and kZ can be
provided—not an easy adjustment to effect.   Some foreign
binnacles were fitted with such an arrangement but this is no
longer the usual practice.

Certainly to have a system of correction which is effective
over a wide range of latitude when dealing with inclination
errors has been avoided for over a hundred years.   Permanent
magnets alone have always been used with the result that steady
compasses soon become unsteady when voyages penetrate

areas of higher or lower latitude. Much instruction and examination has been directed towards encouraging a continuous adjustment of these errors—most to little purpose, because in the event few navigators carry the recommendations into practice. This is a great pity, especially on ships which are fitted with a transmitting magnetic compass as a stand-by against a gyro breakdown. Unless such a compass is repeatedly corrected for inclination errors it becomes useless and were best not fitted in the first place!

The credit account of the sphere correctors is now complete and includes a_1H, e_1H (to eliminate D), b_1H and d_1H (to eliminate E if required), e_1Z and k_1Z (affording a partial correction of inclination error) and finally a favourable contribution to the mean field northward, i.e. an improvement in the value of λ. The reader should be impressed with such an array of beneficial effects on the part of the soft iron spheres directed towards a properly corrected and steady compass. As correctors one might claim that the spheres hold pride of place.

The Single Sphere Corrector

Perhaps there should be mention of those occasions when two soft iron spheres placed at the extremities of the brackets each side of the compass overcompensate and requires one of them to be removed. Theoretically there is nothing wrong with a single sphere located either to port or starboard but it is preferable that two smaller spheres are substituted in order to provide a more uniform correcting field over the area swept out by the compass magnet system. This becomes the more important when the needle system is anything but small, such as a ring magnet frequently used today. Fig. 25 illustrates the uniformity of the field, in terms of lines of equi-potential rather than lines of force, over the area occupied by the needle system.

A single sphere allowed to remain must be very carefully placed with the plane parallel to the deck passing through both the centre of the compass element and the centre of the sphere. Any approximation to this requirement may incur an inadvertent fZ effect giving rise to asymmetry of soft iron about the compass and consequent coefficient induced C. With a sphere on each side the symmetry is restored and makes a further case for the preference of fitting a pair of smaller spheres if these can be made available. If this is still impossible and one sphere has been removed it should be remembered

that although *D* is adequately corrected there occurs, at the
instant of removal, interaction between the heeling error
corrector magnets and the remaining single sphere. This
causes *Q* directed to either port or starboard instead of equally
towards each side. The deviation should be checked on
000°/180° and any change removed by adjusting the athwartship corrector magnets. Moreover, any readjustment of the

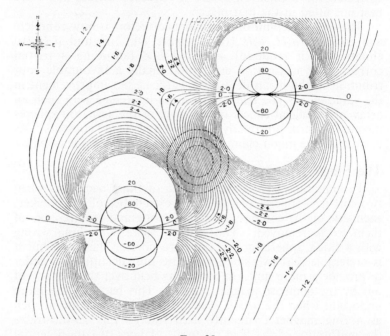

Fig. 25

heeling error magnets implicit upon substantial changes of
latitude would entail repeated checks on this feature of interaction between correctors. Once again, the retention of two
spheres or the provision of smaller ones is always to be
preferred.

Sphere Tests

Much has been said concerning the spheres and the part
they play in equalising and strengthening the northward field
at the compass, as well as removing quadrantal deviation.
Each naturally depends upon the fact that the spheres act

solely as high permeability correctors. In the event of a tendency towards hysteresis or retained magnetism occurring in the spheres it is necessary to be able to detect its presence. If the holding bolts are slackened and the spheres rotated slowly the card should maintain its orientation within a degree or so; any deflection in excess of one degree should be viewed with suspicion and an attempt made to remove the retained magnetism by slight percussion as from one sphere knocking against the other. Tests of this kind should be done only when the ship is securely moored alongside and then preferably if the orientation of the quay is close to the meridian, under which conditions retentivity is the more readily detected owing to any deflection obtained being produced by an end-on effect rather than broadside.

The reader may care to refer to Merchant Shipping Notice M616, paragraph 15 of Appendix 1. Reference is made to what is called the Meldau test and whilst the details of the test cannot be carried out aboard ship it does point out that it is a test which confirms that the magnetic needle system of the compass is well designed, and that the spheres are not too close to the compass.

Summary

If spheres of high permeability material are used, then,

(i) Placed athwartships they cause $-a_1$ and $+e_1$ to eliminate D.

(ii) The correction of quadrantal deviation by sphere correctors is maintained over the complete range of latitude.

(iii) The value of λ is improved in the process.

(iv) Placed anywhere less than 45° from either the fore and aft line or the athwartships line they eliminate D and E should both be present. They cause a_1, e_1, b_1 and d_1.

(v) Placed under the conditions of $D = O$ they serve to reduce both heeling and pitching errors.

(vi) If a third sphere is used it is possible to correct inclination errors in such a way that the correction will be maintained for latitude.

What more could be required of an individual corrector? What other corrector can provide a better package? Most others perform a single function while the spheres are multipurpose. If one recollects that the nature of the terrestrial magnetic field, from which it all starts, resembles closely that of a uniformly magnetised sphere, one may say the same for the sphere corrector whose influence arises almost entirely from the former and displays in turn a field of similar character and shape. The world of the spheres is interwoven and mutually dependent; a comforting thought, aboard a safe ship.

CHAPTER 12

The Conditions for No Deviation - The Ship's Multiplier and the Navigator.

It is not always easy to please everyone at the same time. When people talk about magnetic compass adjustment and advance the theories upon which the practice is based the listener, in this case the reader, is likely to fall into one of three groups. First of all, and by far the most important, those officers aboard ship doing the job of navigating inter alia; secondly, officers qualifying for the next grade certificate either at sea or attending some emporium of nautical learning; and thirdly, a privileged officer, or ex-officer, seeking to attain the highest navigational qualifications which he hopes may enable him to have little more to do with practical seafaring again. In attempting to please members of each group the topic chosen is 'the ship's multiplier' and the ideas which surround its use in practice.

To the uninitiated let it be said that the 'ship's multiplier' is purely a scaling factor used in compass adjustment for the purpose of eliminating what is called heeling error. The routine is very easy, takes about five minutes to explain and five more to put into practice. But this does not satisfy the curious who want to know 'why'. It is this aspect which prompts the writer to consider the ship's multiplier and prevent, if possible, some misconceptions about it remaining in the minds of those who assimilated only a few half truths. There is a further reason for wanting to offer some explanation and this lies in the interest which the examining authority for deck officers certificates of competency shows regarding the nature and purpose of this special scaling number. Qualifying officers should recognise that this topic of discussion is important to them, requires understanding and should no longer be learned by rote through pressure of time. We need to know what the ship's multiplier is; why it is what it is; what its value is and, of course, what its purpose is.

115

The Conditions for No Deviation

One can scarcely begin with the ship's multiplier without considering the *conditions for no deviation* at the compass. If the symbolic notation of the subject is used the ideal and practical conditions for zero deviation can be demonstrated fairly easily but it does demand some familiarity with the special language used. Before attempting to do this, the reader may care to rid his mind of all but the bare essentials of the subject and follow a qualitative argument detailing the ideal conditions to be aimed at. This is useful because too often very close attention is given to the individual magnetic trees and shrubs which tends to conceal the overall shape and character of the compass wood. Confusion remains when the wood cannot be seen for the trees.

A Wooden Boat with a Magnetic Compass

The starting point would seem to be a properly gimballed magnetic compass installed in some kind of non-magnetic craft. Clearly, such a compass points to magnetic north simply because there is nowhere else for it to point. But this obvious statement requires a closer appreciation than the platitude suggests. Firstly, the pervading influence is the earth's magnetic field denoted by T in the vector diagram. A freely-suspended magnetic needle would tend to respond to this influence. But the compass is not freely suspended; in fact it remains substantially horizontal because its centre of gravity is secured, in manufacture, below the pivot point. This is obvious to the navigator because he needs the instrument for steering courses and taking bearings in the horizontal plane. It follows that the magnetic compass derives its directive property from the horizontal component (H) of the earth's field. Provided that the gimbal system supporting the compass is efficient it follows that the needle will lie in the magnetic meridian regardless of the attitude of the craft and we have, in its simplest terms, the ideal condition for no deviation. Furthermore, one may assert that the directive field strength northward is the same on all headings and for all reasonable attitudes of roll and pitch simply because there is no reason or cause why it should be otherwise.

Let it be made clear what is meant by craft attitude. Freedom must naturally exist to pursue any prescribed course of which there are 360 alternatives. Secondly, the nature of the craft and the medium in which it floats demand further reasonable attitudes of roll and pitch. The pivot and jewel arrangement provides for the former and the gimbal mechanism for the latter. These points may be accepted in further discussion. The reader will no doubt appreciate that, although not applicable to ships, aircraft compasses require the full 360° freedom about all three axes of movement unless one or other is suppressed for special reasons.

Resolution of the Earth's Total Field

Accepting that the earth's magnetic field is usually oblique with reference to the sensible horizon most navigators are aware of its simple resolution into horizontal (H) and vertical (Z) components. These are shown in the vector diagram and are components of field strength independent of the ship. They are governed purely by geographical location and nothing more. At this point an extension to the resolution of field components is introduced because it prepares the background against which ship-created disturbances may be superposed. The horizontal component H is resolved into two separate components; one directed fore and aft and the other athwartships. The former is designated X and the latter Y. At an horizontally balanced compass the pre-existing field of the earth is therefore represented by three mutually perpendicular vectors X, Y and Z. This serves as the background or stage setting, and is basic to the study of deviation. Owing to the fact that the ship's orientation has now been included and bearing in mind the sole existence of the earth's field (T) it follows that while Z remains a constant vector the strengths (and therefore the lengths) of vectors X and Y will change from heading to heading. Every attitude of course will have its individual components X and Y combining with Z to describe the resultant T. The process is reversible: T resolved into X, Y and Z, or X, Y and Z, supporting T. At any instant, on some particular course, one can examine the situation at the compass in terms of the three components. The vector diagram shows this clearly for a non-magnetic craft heading on some unspecified north-westerly course such that the fore and after component of T is directed forward (X), the athwartship component directed to starboard (Y) and the vertical component (Z) directed downward, implicit to the vessel being somewhere in the northern hemisphere. Since the compass remains undeviated the resultant of X and Y is the undeviated

H towards magnetic north. Since also, the compass remains substantially horizontal throughout, it follows that any of an infinite number of combinations of heading, roll and pitch can be imagined in terms of appropriate values of X, Y and Z. Always the three components support the original T and its undeviated component H to which the compass needles respond.

Resolution of the Ship's Field

If the ship's structure, instead of being non-magnetic, is largely made of ferrous material then the ideal conditions outlined above no longer obtain. Disturbing influences, caused either by the hull structure and/or local superstructures in the vicinity of the compass, give rise to a magnetic field which must be compounded with the earth's field to predict the direction of the resultant whose horizontal component will ultimately direct the compass needles. Although the orientation of such a ship field with reference to the plane of the deck remains unknown the effect of it may be described and superposed upon X, Y and Z by some diagnostic process if only its *strength* were constant. This ship's field, however, alters in magnitude with heading and geographic location so that the problem of appreciating what happens is almost intractable until further analytical thought is given to the nature of the ship's magnetisation.

Magnetic Character of the Ship

At this point it is convenient to speculate on how the first theorists gained some order out of apparent chaos when considering the character of ship magnetisation. Although, in the case of some iron ships of the last century, it was convenient to think of the ship's magnetisation as purely the result of permanent low permeability magnetisation (hard iron) this simple concept was both inadequate theoretically and practically. One could not omit the possibility, indeed probability, that part of the magnetisation owed its origin to transient high permeability effects (soft iron) dependent upon ship orientation relative to the earth's field which then induced magnetism into the ship. Clearly, a distinction between the effects of hard iron and soft iron magnetisation was desirable if only to acknowledge that the actual condition was caused neither solely by the one nor solely by the other but in fact lay somewhere between the two. It is this uncertainty which led the early theorists to state that the character of ship magnetisation consisted partly of hard iron and partly of soft iron; the former permanent and the latter variable.

Further Resolution of the Ship Field

The reader is at the point where the ambient field at the compass has been resolved into X, Y and Z components due solely to the earth's influence, with some undefined and unknown magnetic field caused by the ship's magnetic material. This unknown influence is attributed partly to hard iron and partly to soft iron, but no more is known about it. What proportion of each is unknown and, at any given compass position, its orientation is also unknown. The proposition is now put that whatever may be the orientation and strength of the *ship's magnetic field* there is every advantage to be gained by considering it resolved into three mutually perpendicular components related to *ship orientated directions*. The choice here is obvious—one component of field strength parallel to the deck in the fore and aft line, a second parallel to the deck in the athwartships line and the third perpendicular to the deck. If it is then remembered that each of these component field strengths has a dual origin, namely the effects of both hard and soft iron magnetisation, one can, for simplicity, denote the former by a capital symbol and the latter by a lower case symbol. In this sense the fore and aft field vector can be designated $P+p$, the athwartship vector $Q+q$ and the third in the to-keel line as $R+r$.

Two Frames of Reference

The resolution and clarification of the magnetic condition at the compass is now almost complete. Both the earth's ambient field and the ship's own disturbing field are resolved into X, Y and Z; and, $P+p$, $Q+q$ and $R+r$ respectively. The first group is related to the sensible horizon and the second group to the plane of the deck. There are two different frames of reference which need to be reconciled. The option exists to transfer either one to the other because provision must be made for various attitudes of roll and pitch in addition to heading. Since the orientations of X, Y and Z relate to the sensible horizon it seems appropriate to adjust $P+p$, $Q+q$ and $R+r$ to the same frame of reference by reducing each by the cosine of the inclination which the deck makes, individually for each, with the true horizontal plane. Although this is slightly over-simplified it is justified in the case of ships where the angles of pitch, roll and tilt are never excessive and the cosines of these relatively small angles approach unity. The total disturbed field at the compass may now be considered as resolved into three mutually perpendicular components: X+P+p, Y+Q+q and Z+R+r.

The Compass Doctor

It is useful to pause for a moment and think again about the compass wood. The components X, Y and Z (earth's field) have added to them P+p, Q+q and R+r (ship's field) and the status quo has been seriously upset to an extent which is practically unpredictable although the concept of the three perpendicular components points very clearly to the means by which order might be restored.

Mixing the metaphors a little further it is not difficult to appreciate how a medical practitioner operates by making specific tests appropriate to a general area of illness, establishes certain symptoms, confirms the disease and then prescribes the medicine. The same diagnostic approach is used by the compass doctor for which purpose he makes special tests on certain headings to diagnose either the presence or absence of one sign or the other, of P, Q, R, p, q, and r individually. This organised search for symptoms is what the subject is all about; a detective process in which, for the moment, the detail does not matter but the line of approach does. It follows that if there is a systematic routine which enables the compass doctor to diagnose the presence of any one component of force in terms of deviation he is immediately in possession of the means by which it can be eliminated. Such is the practice of adjust- ment: organised detection, diagnosis, and the medicine (or poison!) to eliminate each ship component separately.

The Final Compromise

The clue to the end product lies in the vector diagram shown in, Fig. 26. The detection of P+p, Q+q and R+r and their reduction to zero restores the ideal condition for no deviation, i.e. the compass is then affected, once more, solely by X, Y and Z where each has its full value appropriate to the ambient T for the instantaneous attitude of the ship. But there is another possibility, and this lies in scaling each of the vectors X, Y and Z up or down by the same *proportion*. Assume for the moment a scaling factor called λ somewhat less than unity. If each of the vectors is scaled down to the products λX, λY and λZ it follows that whilst the size of the cuboid in Fig. 26 is reduced its *shape is retained* with the result that the direction of λT is *unaltered*. It then follows that λH

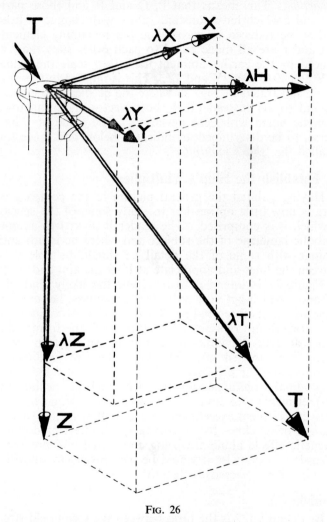

FIG. 26

continues to direct the compass needles towards magnetic north for all attitudes of the ship but with slightly diminished field strength. The inference to be drawn from this conclusion

E

lies in the fact that whilst it might be desirable to reduce P+p, Q+q and R+r, each to zero, they *need not in the event be necessarily eliminated completely* if they can be made to alter the vectors X, Y and Z in the *same sense and in the same proportion*. This means that P, Q and R and those parts of p, q and r which have constant values with change of heading need to be reduced to zero while the remaining elements of p, q and r are all made equal to each other such that, when induced by the earth's ambient field, they scale the values of X, Y and Z to λX, λY and λZ. This is implied in the smaller cuboid illustrated in Fig. 26 where the needles of the compass respond to λH instead of H; both vectors pointing towards magnetic north with zero deviation. The value of λ has, of course, to be determined as indicated below and, once found, is called the *'ship's multiplier'*.

To Establish the Ship's Multiplier

Having painted the general picture of the compass wood there is now little option but to study some of the specimens of which it is comprised. The reader is invited to accept the symbolic language of the subject and where he is not entirely familiar with some of the detail he should be able to read between the lines and appreciate at least the aim and purpose.

Figure 27 is intended to represent the likely kind of disturbances which act at a well placed compass, i.e. one placed in the fore and aft centre-line. Two fore and aft components of field strength are represented by P and cZ, the former due to hard iron and the latter to soft iron, which, from random choice, are directed aft. The Q component is directed to starboard and the presence of the continuity of transverse and longitudinal structure is illustrated by high permeability (soft iron) elements −e and −a respectively. *Magnetically* the transverse element exceeds the fore and aft element (−e> −a) because, being closer to the compass, this effect predominates. Magnetic effects alone are being considered and not physical dimensions, otherwise it would be paradoxical to suggest that the ship's beam exceeds its length!

Lambda (λ)

By definition, λ is the ratio between the mean field strength northward at the compass and the earth's ambient horizontal field component (H). To derive an expression for this Fig. 26 is used to express the field strength northward on the four cardinal headings separately. A little intentional licence has been taken in the matter of the strict sign convention in the hope that some readers may more easily understand the conclusions reached.

Heading north: field strength northward	$= H - P - cZ - aH$			
Heading east: field strength northward	$= H$		$-Q$	$-eH$
Heading south: field strength northward	$= H + P + cZ - aH$			
Heading west: field strength northward	$= H$		$+Q$	$-eH$
Total field strength northward	$= 4)4H$	$-2aH$		$-2eH$

$$\text{Mean field strength northward} = \frac{H}{} \qquad \frac{-aH}{2} \qquad \frac{-eH}{2}$$

$$= H - \left(\frac{a+e}{2}\right) H$$

$$= H \left(1 - \frac{a+e}{2}\right)$$

By definition above λ is the proportion which this mean field bears to the undisturbed H, i.e.

$$\lambda = \frac{H \left(1 - \frac{a+e}{2}\right)}{H} = 1 - \frac{a+e}{2}$$

The reader will note firstly, that the mean directing field remains unaffected by P, cZ and Q because, being constant vectors in a given latitude, they act favourably on certain headings and unfavourably on those opposite. Secondly, the vectors aH and eH both act unfavourably on opposite headings and therefore accumulate to cause an overall deficiency in the mean field strength northward. The final expression for λ confirms this and suggests that it should not be excessively low or the compass would be useless! Fortunately, the placing of the soft iron spheres each side of the compass helps to restore part of this deficiency.

Lambda$_2$ (λ_2)

As suggested, the sphere correctors when secured in their proper positions on brackets athwart the compass serve two purposes. They eliminate a positive coefficient D and increase

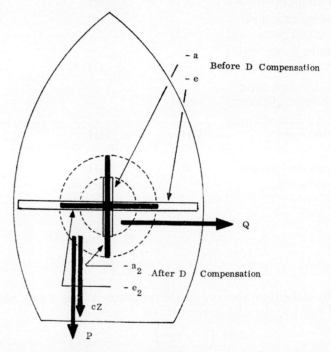

Fig. 27

the mean field strength northward. The precise manner in which they do this does not matter but the diagram (Fig. 27) shows that in the process —e and —a are equated and are, for convenience, designated —e$_2$ and —a$_2$. It follows that the extension of the element —a to —a$_2$ decreases the mean field northward, while the contraction of —e to —e$_2$ increases the mean field northward. It may be shown that the latter exceeds the former so that on balance there is an improvement. Since for D to be zero —a$_2$ = —e$_2$ either the one or the other may be substituted for —a and —e in the expression for λ. Let the new ratio of comparison be designated by λ_2, then,

$$\lambda = 1 - \frac{a + e}{2}$$

$$\lambda_2 = 1 - \frac{e_2 + e_2}{2}$$

$$\lambda_2 = 1 - e_2$$

In a sense this expresses a special value of λ, being the ratio which the mean field strength northwards bears to the ambient H when, and only when, D is zero, i.e. properly corrected. This special value of λ_2 is the *'ship's multiplier'*. To appreciate its further significance it is useful to consider the ship inclined.

The Heeled Condition

Figure 28 indicates a vessel in the heeled condition with examples of likely components of field parallel to the plane of the compass arising from two field components perpendicular to the deck and one parallel to the deck. Two out of the three

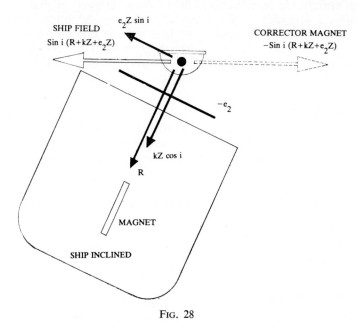

SHIP FIELD

$e_2Z \sin i$

Sin i $(R + kZ + e_2Z)$

CORRECTOR MAGNET

$-\sin i \ (R + kZ + e_2Z)$

$-e_2$

$kZ \cos i$

R

MAGNET

SHIP INCLINED

FIG. 28

are attributed to soft iron ($kZ \cos i$ and $e_2Z \sin i$) while the third represents the to-keel component due to hard iron (R). If the heel is not excessive the cosine functions can be read as unity and, in the case shown, the total *deviating field* is R sin i +kZsin i +e$_2$Zsin i, or sin i (R +kZ +e$_2$Z). Clearly, the ideal solution to such disturbing vectors is to instal appropriate soft iron and hard iron correctors to eliminate the respective components. Whilst this is not entirely impossible no effective provision is normally made for doing it and in practice a compromise occurs by using a permanent magnet suitably placed to cause a deviating component of opposite sign equal to the sum of those which exist. Fig. 28 illustrates therefore, the proper position of such a corrector whose horizontal component of field strength must be −sin i (R +kZ +e$_2$Z). Of course, this is not difficult if the ship were heeled on some heading, preferably close to north or south, and the *change* of deviation caused by the heel eliminated when it appears. The necessity of transferring ballast and/or bunkers for the purpose is, however, a nuisance to be avoided and magnetically the condition should be reconsidered with the ship upright, so that the total field acting vertically is made to assume a strength (λZ) which produces no deviation when the ship *subsequently* heels. At first sight it may be thought that the vertical field, excluding the ambient Z, should be obviously reduced to zero. But first thoughts are not always correct!

Vessel Upright (μ_2)

Figure 29 represents the ship illustrated in Fig. 28 restored to the upright condition with the corrector magnet still in position, at the *same distance*, below the compass. Bearing in mind that the transverse element of soft iron after the correction of D (i.e. −e$_2$), being now horizontal, is no longer induced by Z the sum of all *vertical forces* at the compass can be listed.

Earth's ambient field	=	Z	
Ship Field	=	+R	+kZ
Field of Magnet	=	−R	−kZ −e$_2$Z
Total Mean Vertical Field	=	Z	−e$_2$Z

If this is now compared with the ambient vertical field of the earth (Z) we find the ratio is (Z−e$_2$Z)/Z = 1−e$_2$. This ratio is designated μ_2 and simply defines the ratio of vertical field strengths necessary to *achieve* a proper placing of the vertical corrector magnets.

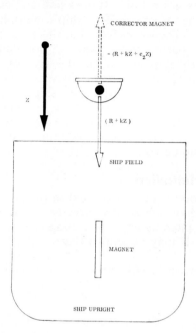

$$-(R + kZ + e_2Z)$$

$$(R + kZ)$$

SHIP FIELD

MAGNET

SHIP UPRIGHT

FIG. 29

The Numerical Identity of λ_2 and μ_2

Since, after the correction of D, $-a_2 = -e_2$, it follows that if these vertical forces were compared under the conditions of pitch instead of roll then $\mu_2 = 1-a_2 = 1-e_2$. This demonstrates that when D is zero and the magnet is secured at the correct height to eliminate heeling error, it also eliminates pitching error, i.e. *all inclination errors are corrected.* It also emphasises that if D is *not* zero then the correction can only be effected for either roll or pitch but not both. Clearly, it is sensible to ensure that D is zero or negligible.

The definition $\mu_2 = 1-e_2$ is numerically identical with λ_2, N.B. $\lambda_2 = 1-e_2$ above. This, it must be recognised, is not a fortuitous coincidence but a vital necessity *to preserve the conditions for no deviation* and points the way to the practical method of eliminating inclination errors without physically inclining the vessel and causing unnecessary inconvenience.

What this amounts to is to make μ_2 by *definition* equal *numerically* to λ_2 after which one may assert that inclination errors have been got rid of! It does not, and cannot, alter the *definition* of either λ_2 or μ_2. The 'ship's multiplier' throughout is λ_2 and not μ_2. The writer feels that this point is so frequently misunderstood, partly understood, or not understood at all that it is worth emphasising at the risk of being tedious. For instance, to say that λ_2 is the same as μ_2 is wrong; in fact meaningless. To say that μ_2 is the ship's multiplier is also wrong, because it isn't. To say that μ_2 is found or calculated in some way or other is nonsense. To say that μ_2 by *definition* is made to be λ_2 *numerically* is to state the condition required to correct inclination error.

Alternative Multipliers

The suggestion made above, that in the event of D remaining uncorrected (which is silly, because it's so easy to get rid of) then either pitching error or rolling error can be corrected but not both. It may be shown that:

$$\text{To correct heeling error} \quad \mu = \lambda\left(1 - \frac{a-e}{2\lambda}\right)$$

$$\text{i.e. } \mu = \lambda(1 - \text{Sin D})$$

$$\text{To correct pitching error} \quad \mu = \lambda\left(1 + \frac{a-e}{2\lambda}\right)$$

$$\text{i.e. } \mu = \lambda(1 + \text{Sin D})$$

If a choice were to be made between the two preference should be given to the former scaling factor, namely $\lambda(1 - \text{Sin D})$ because the unsteadiness promoted by uncorrected heeling error predominates. Nevertheless, it is much better to eliminate coefficient D and not have need to contend with alternative multipliers.

The Heeling Error Instrument

The reader, preferably the navigator or master aboard ship, may wish to question where all this leads to? Where is the practice? What can be done, instead of all the talk? How can he accept the roll of compass Doctor and effect a cure? It is easy provided that there is a heeling error instrument aboard.

This instrument is a pivoted magnetised needle as shown in Fig. 30 fitted with a sliding weight and mounted in a suitable case with spirit level attached and a chain from which it may be suspended. If the instrument is set up, unlocked to make it sensitive, it will then respond to a vertical field by dipping one way or the other. Clearly, the sliding weight can be adjusted so that the needle lies in a position of horizontal equilibrium. Equidistant graduations are marked on the needle and these,

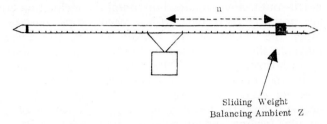

Sliding Weight
Balancing Ambient Z

FIG. 30

if counted from the fulcrum to the sliding weight, afford an arbitrary measure of vertical field strength. The instrument can thus be used to *compare* vertical fields in the direct ratio of successive scale readings.

The End Product—Correction of Heeling Error with the Ship Upright

The steps which should be taken to use the heeling error instrument aboard ship are very simple and do not take long to do. Each operation is numbered in the correct sequence.

(i) The instrument should be set up in a convenient spot ashore, away from the ship, railway lines, cranes and other magnetic material, levelled with the spirit level (an empty orange box is useful to stand the instrument on), orientated approximately north-south, and the sliding weight adjusted (on the south or unmarked end in the northern hemisphere, and vice versa) to bring the needle perfectly horizontal. The scale reading of the position of the weight is read and noted. This reading is multiplied by an assumed value of the ship's multiplier (λ_2) of 0·8 and the weight reset slightly towards the centre to the new value.

(ii) Aboard ship, on the swinging ground (provided that the conditions are calm), the ship is put on a course of 090° or 270° (to eliminate a second order cause of heeling error which need not be discussed here) and the compass bowl removed from the binnacle. The instrument is then placed at the *same height* formerly occupied by the compass by suspending it from a wooden batten across the top of the binnacle.

(iii) If the needle, preferably though not necesssarily orientated north-south, now remains horizontal the inclination errors are properly corrected. If the needle dips one way or other the height of the bucket holding the corrector magnets should be raised or lowered until the needle is again horizontal. It may be necessary to add or subtract from the number of magnets already in the bucket; possibly even to reverse those which exist. Once the needle is level the job is done, and all the causes of semi-circular heeling and pitching errors are eliminated. The correction is valid *only* for the latitude in which it is effected and must be repeated when the latitude has substantially changed.

To Get the Record Straight

There are a few points which remain to be clarified so that navigators who intend to employ this useful method of correcting inclination errors appreciate its full potential.

(*a*) The levelling process, described in (i) above, needs to be done only once. Since the scale reading of the sliding weight is proportional to Z the corresponding setting of the weight to eliminate Z can be calculated for any other position in the world by using the Z chart (No. 5378). This avoids the necessity of going ashore and permits the instrument to be used on a calm day anywhere at sea. If the original setting to eliminate Z is n_1 and the setting is required in some new geographic location (n_2) then:

$$n_2 = n_1 \times \frac{Z_2}{Z_1}$$

Clearly, the sliding weight must be put on the north end of the needle if Z_2 is located in the southern hemisphere where the ambient Z is negative.

(*b*) The ship's multiplier (λ_2) is reasonably assumed to have a value of 0·8 or 0·9 because it is a lengthy experimental process to determine its precise value. The proper setting for the original situation is therefore $n_1 \times \lambda_2$ and for any subsequent position $n_2 \times \lambda_2$.

(c) It has been pointed out that it is desirable to assume either an east or west course for the reason stated in (ii) above. The correction for inclination error can, however, be done alongside the quay in advance of going to the swinging ground. No great harm arises provided the heading alongside happens to be no less than 40° to 50° from north or south. In fact it is often more desirable to effect the correction alongside, in advance, and thereby ensure a steadier compass should the swinging ground be in an open sea area such as the Bristol Channel.

(d) Sometimes a rather loose or casual procedure is adopted whereby the original 'shore' setting (n_1 or n_2) for the sliding weight is retained and used at the compass without making an actual adjustment for λ_2. In this event the magnets are in their correct position provided that the needle of the heeling error instrument has the end with the weight on it slightly depressed from the horizontal. This procedure amounts to the same thing as using the scaling factor directly but is not recommended because the extra trouble entailed in adjusting the position of the weight is no great burden and removes the element of guesswork otherwise necessary.

(e) In the event of using the method outlined to correct inclination errors when the ship is located fortuitously on the magnetic equator ($Z = O$) the needle of the instrument is used at the compass position *without* the sliding weight.

The Heeling Error Instrument and—You

It seems one should face reality. The conditions for no deviation have been mentioned; they exist and cannot be denied. They may not be understood, but that's not the point. They involve the 'ship's multiplier' and an explanation has been offered for its need, its value, and the part it plays when correcting inclination error using the heeling error instrument. Where does the master or navigator stand in relation to the efficient performance of his magnetic compass against the day when there is a gyro breakdown?

He can, of course, produce a steady compass with the ship rolling heavily on courses near to north or south by a tentative adjustment of the heeling error correctors. This is fair enough; it is quick, easy and effective and preferable to looking the other way and doing nothing about it. What then of the heeling error instrument? Should every ship have one? The answer is clearly, yes. The reader now knows what it's for and how to use it; so there's no excuse. The correction can be effected quietly, alongside, with the ship upright and the compass will be steady as soon as the ship begins to roll and pitch. Trouble has been prevented *before* it can occur. All this is good, especially now that the background has been filled in for those who were not aware of it before.

And yet, some will say, 'I've never seen it done'—'We didn't have the instrument'—or, with greater presumption— 'No one does this at sea'. Well, we've had all this before. Naturally, the navigator hasn't seen it done if he wasn't present to see it. Make a point, next time, of being there and watching. The adjuster will often do it before 'stand-by' when you are usually below decks. Better still, do it yourself, and if there is no heeling error instrument on board, indent for one. But don't say, 'No one ever does this aboard ship'. You don't know what other folk do on other ships! And bear this in mind, the D.T.I. encourages its use or they would not be so interested and emphasise it in examinations directed towards a high level of competence. Both confidence and the competence which inspires it encourage a measure of compass-wisdom. This, it is hoped, leads to greater safety at sea by having at all times possible a properly corrected and, therefore, *steady* compass.

CHAPTER 13

1872 - 1972: A Century of Compass Work at the Examinations.

With the introduction of new examination syllabuses for navigating officers the writer describes part of the background which relates to the Standard of Compass Knowledge required from qualifying officers during the last hundred years. Intending candidates are made acquainted with some of the changes which have taken place in compass work and warned that a theoretical ability together with a mastery of compass computations have not hitherto produced a comparable degree of competence aboard ship. Has examination in compass work fulfilled its designed purpose?

DURING the 14 years which elapsed between 1836 and 1850 the mathematical analysis of the deviation at a magnetic compass was established by the interested scientists of the day. It was left principally to the late Lord Kelvin, many years later (1879) to devise the system of correction used today and to design a binnacle which housed all the necessary correctors conveniently close to the compass.

The First Hint of Examinations

In 1869 the Board of Trade instituted a voluntary examination on the subject of compass deviation so that masters of iron ships could appreciate the nature of the ship's disturbing influences, learn to detect their presence and to know the means by which they could be eliminated. The examination was conducted at Liverpool and was encouraged in order that knowledge of compass deviation should be given due importance by serving masters, shipowners and underwriters.

Three years later, in 1872, the examination on compass deviation became compulsory for all examinees taking the examination for a Master's Certificate. The syllabus was laid down explicitly in terms of 19 questions, and the candidate was required to answer correctly at least eight of these. The substance of the questions bears a remarkable resemblance to

133

many which are asked today although some topics in the present examination would have been unrecognisable to the qualifying masters of a hundred years ago.

A Century of Compass Work

Now that precisely a hundred years have elapsed since compass work was compulsorily introduced into the statutory examination syllabus for deck officers it might be thought time to see what has been achieved. Certainly the examinations have changed with the passing years but this is not to say that they have necessarily improved; if by that it is meant that they are more difficult. Throughout it may fairly be said that qualifying officers have been required to detect the sign and amount of deviation on specified headings, understand the cause of it, and knowing this be competent to remove it. Unfortunately the simple issues have often been obscured by theoretical and largely academic problems barely connected with practice. The result of this has been that examinees have had to wrestle with many unrealistic questions as well as dealing with more appropriate ones. The sense of proportion has to some extent been lost so that it may be questioned whether the actual purpose of the examination has been entirely maintained as originally intended.

Periodically the examining authority has revised and up-dated the examinations. Of late years revisions of syllabuses have occurred at intervals of 20 years, in 1932, 1952 and 1972. It might be thought significant that new syllabuses in compass work should appear 100 years after the original one of 1872. Qualifying officers need to know what is now involved for the obvious reason that they must satisfy their examiners. Since most changes relate to what has happened in the past a few words in this connection are not amiss.

The Last Forty Years

From 1932 to 1952, candidates for a Master's Foreign-Going certificate were examined theoretically and practically on the magnetic compass. This was a period, which included the war years, during which the subject was treated realistically in the sense that the theory of deviation in terms of the approximate coefficients and the causes of heeling error was studied and every candidate was required to effect a proper adjustment of the deviascope model as part of the oral examination. The subject was on the whole well balanced and not unnecessarily complicated. The general theory of magneto-statics was not included, nor did gyro compass work feature in the syllabus except at Extra Master level and then only in an elementary form.

In 1952 further revisions and additions were made to the extent that for the First Mate's Foreign-Going certificate an elementary knowledge of ship magnetism was introduced and for the Master's certificate the theory of magneto-statics and a knowledge of gyro compass theory were added. At First Mate level it was clear that the introduction of magnetism was to fulfill the apparent need for some preparatory work as a preliminary for the more specific details of compass deviation which would be required for Master to follow some two years later. The writer submits that in the event this was never satisfactorily achieved because the interval between the two certificates prevented effective continuity. Secondly, and the more important, was the fact that high and low permeability magnetic disturbances were required to be studied in a manner quite unsuitable to the subsequent learning of the theory of the deviations at a magnetic compass. For instance, examinees were questioned upon the effect of—'a piece of horizontal soft iron' (or, vertical soft iron, etc.) placed near to a compass, orientated as stated with reference to the fore and aft line. The intention of such questions is clear but the oversimplification was unjustified, unreal and very little help to the proper study of the deviating fields at a magnetic compass. The approach was unsatisfactory to the extent that such materials don't exist near to the compass.

Such questions tended to instil and then perpetuate false ideas concerning certain structures aboard ship, such as masts, derricks, funnels, pillars, bulkheads and beams and to identify these with high rather than low permeability magnetic effects for no apparent reason. Such questions were kept largely divorced from the general theory of deviation, presumably to keep the concepts easy, so that instead of being a useful preliminary and a solid foundation these exercises weakened the subject. The questions were invariably descriptive with no useful quantitative results forthcoming. In fact, the experiment at the First Mate level from 1952 to 1972 is analogous to some of the work which was done for Master between 1932 and 1952 where for many years quite undue importance was attached to the 'direction of the ship's head in the building yard'. Even today instruction is sometimes given which relates the field disturbances at a compass to 'the building yard heading' on the basis that H induction alone is considered with the effects of Z almost ignored, when in fact the latter is often the predominating influence. Many of these odd ideas persisted for far too long and should have been abandoned in favour of the formal theory of deviation which was available throughout from Admiralty sources.

It seems that from 1932 to 1952 for Master, and from 1952 to 1972 for First Mate the examining authorities tended to encourage a pattern of compass knowledge (which the navigation schools had necessarily to follow) which ignored certain basic concepts about the causes of compass deviation, namely that they should be expressed in terms of P, Q, R and the parameters a, b, c, d, e, f, g, h and k. With this in mind one can appreciate how candidates at the Extra Master level of examination are generally encouraged to treat with the formal theory almost as if it is something new instead of being established for more than 130 years.

From 1952 to date the additions of magneto-statics and gyro work have made greater demands on examinees. Once again the intention behind the inclusion of quantitative magneto-statics may have been well founded; the general must precede the particular. Is this always essential? The navigator doesn't design a compass, so why should he know the value of its magnetic moment? When does a navigator need to compare the pole strength or magnetic moment of two otherwise similar magnets? And more important, where does this arise in the study and subsequent removal of deviation aboard ship in the cause of safety? Apart from a few quantitative relationships, which may justifiably be stated, the numerical problems attached to magneto-statics afford little help in the study of the theory of deviation and still less on practical adjustment, which is surely what the subject is all about.

If one is sceptical about the efficacy of introducing magneto-statics to the Master's syllabus in 1952 only praise can be given to the inclusion of gyro compass work from that date. From the time that the marine gyro compass was invented in 1908 increasing numbers of ships have been fitted with it. The examining authority were wise to include the gyro compass but it seems that over the last 20 years the preliminary work at First Mate level and the more advanced at Master grade have suffered from a peculiar interpretation of the syllabus at the examinations. Although there have been many useful and very appropriate questions asked it seems that there have been occasions when the examiner didn't know what to ask, set something oddly associated with the subject and waited to see what happened when the hapless examinee was faced with it. A case in point concerned a gyroscope at the equator with its spin axis pointing east/west and constrained to the horizontal; what might its subsequent motion reveal? Although this may constitute an interesting problem it remains to wonder why it was asked, how it could ever be constrained in this fashion aboard a rolling ship, and what it has to do with marine gyro compasses? Likewise, the candidate who was faced with a Sperry Mk E 14 compass and asked to consider the effect of attaching the ballistic frame to the rotor case fractionally westward of the true vertical through the system! It seems a little unfair to place upon the examinee the burden of speculating about the impossible!

The 1972 Compass Examination

Officers at sea coming ashore to prepare for their statutory examinations at the present time face new syllabuses as laid down in the latest handbook. At the Second Mate level qualifying officers are now expected to have an understanding of general magnetism to fulfill the requirements of the appropriate part of the General Physics paper. Some simple calculations are necessary and an appreciation of terrestrial magnetism is required. At the First Mate level compass work as such is not included although the syllabus does contain a reference to the effects which current carrying wires have in the vicinity of the compass. It is not clear at this stage what the examining authority requires in this connection. Candidates can hardly be expected to discourse in terms of the theory of deviation when this subject is rightly reserved for an intensive study at Master level. It seems that this item is an unwanted survivor from the previous 1952 syllabus.

At the Master Foreign Going stage compass work comes into its own and at least maintains, and sometimes exceeds, the standard set in the 1952 examinations. Basically the three topics are included; general magneto-statics, the theory and practice of compass deviation and the theory and construction of modern gyro compasses. It is emphasised that a more detailed knowledge of the principles of magnetism is required than that which is included in the General Physics paper for Second Mate. The only addition to the subject matter is 'the simple treatment of the effects of de-gaussing'. Once again it is not possible to gauge accurately what the authority will set at the examinations when they interpret their own syllabus but it is certain that the standard required will be no less than hitherto and the 50% pass mark for the paper remains unchanged.

The syllabus for Master in compass work is like other syllabuses in so far that it is purely an examination syllabus and not a course content list. Certain items appear almost at random while others are more related to each other. For instance, one paragraph labelled (b) on page 47 consists of one sentence—'The period of a suspended magnet vibrating in the earth's field.'

It conjures up quite odd impressions to anyone with imagination, means very little by itself, is somewhat misleading and gives little clue to its presence at that point in the syllabus. In the following paragraph, (c), there appears—'the construction of the magnetic compass and binnacle, the effect of constraining a compass needle to the horizontal plane'. It is difficult to reconcile the two topics or if any connection between them is intended; probably not. The effect of constraining a compass needle to the horizontal plane is presumably to do just that, and make it useable as a compass. One is left to wonder what such a statement, which originated 102 years ago in the first volunary syllabus, actually means. If by the phrase is meant—'the method by which a magnetic compass is made to remain substantially within the horizontal plane'— it would make more sense. And then concerning a free gyroscope the syllabus lists—'the effect of the earth's rotation on a free gyroscope'—the intention here is understood but the words used in the printed syllabus prompt the comment—'it (the earth's rotation) has no effect on a free gyroscope which is why it is so useful'! Another phrase—'Drift and tilt, damping.' Disociated items like these appear together at random for no apparent reason. Certainly to write a clear and concise syllabus can be no easy matter. It must not be too vague nor too detailed but it should mean what it says and in all fairness measure up to the same standard of English required by examinees as detailed on page 1 of the new handbook.

S.I. Units

Perhaps the biggest change which qualifying officers can expect in the 1972 examinations lies in the changeover to the use of S.I. (Système International d'Unités) units. In certain subjects there is a simplification; in compass work there is only unnecessary complication which arises from the fact that magnetic quantities in the new system must be derived from electrical quantities. Some of the magnetic quantities are now so minute that they need to be expressed by using multipliers of the order of 10^{-4}, 10^{-5}, 10^{-6}, etc. The area affected most by the change to S.I. units is the study of magneto-statics. The theory of compass deviation fortunately remains largely unaffected.

Summary Table of S.I. Units and Equivalent C.G.S. Units

Quantity	S.I. Unit	Equivalent in C.G.S. units
Length (l)	metre (m)	10^2 cm
Mass (m)	kilogramme (kg)	10^3 gm
Time (t)	second (s)	—
Force (F)	Newton (N)	10^5 dynes
Magnetic field strength (H)	ampere per metre (A/m)	$4\pi 10^{-3}$ oersteds
Magnetic flux (Φ)	weber (Wb)	10^8 maxwells
Magnetic pole strength (m)	weber (Wb)	$10^8/4\pi$ unit poles
Magnetic flux density (B)	tesla (T) or weber per square metre (Wb/m²)	10^4 gauss
Magnetic permeability	henry per metre (H/m)	$10^7/4\pi$

A considerable number of definitions in magneto-statics need to be relearned and, of course, the units are entirely different. The table of equivalents shows these differences clearly.

In order to make the implications more clear a simple example is chosen and the computation made firstly in the C.G.S. system of units (centimetre, gramme, second) and then using the S.I. units.

Simple Example Using C.G.S. Units

A north magnetic pole of strength 24 *units is located* 6 *cm from a south magnetic pole which it attracts with a force of* 16 *dynes. Calculate the strength of the south magnetic pole.*

In the C.G.S. system the unit pole is defined as one which repels a similar unit pole placed 1 cm from it with a force of 1 dyne. Assuming that the permeability of the gap between them is taken as unity then,

$$F = \frac{m_1\, m_2}{\mu d^2} = \frac{m_1 m_2}{d^2}$$

$$m_2 = \frac{Fd^2}{m_1} = \frac{16 \times 6^2}{24} = 24 \text{ units}$$

Similar Example Using S.I. Units

A north magnetic pole of strength 3×10^{-6} *Wb is located* 6 *cm from a south magnetic pole which it attracts with a force of* 4×10^{-4} *Newtons. Calculate the strength of the south magnetic pole.*

In the S.I. system the unit pole cannot be defined as simply as that shown above. The pole strength (m) is defined in terms of the flux which emanates from it. The unit is the Weber (Wb). Magnetic field strength (H) is measured in derived units, namely Ampere turns per metre (A/m). The force that would be exerted on a unit pole located within the magnetic field would be expressed in terms of force, namely Newtons (N), which would be numerically identical with the field strength.

$$F = mH$$

If the total flux emanating from a pole is m Wb then since this spreads evenly in all directions the flux density (B) on the surface of a spherical shell of radius r is given by,

$$B = \frac{m}{4\pi\, r^2} \text{ Wb/m}^2$$

Now, field strength (H) is given by,

$$H = \frac{B}{\mu} = \frac{m}{4\pi\, r^2\, \mu} \text{ A/m}$$

Where μ is the absolute permeability of the intervening medium. It may be shown that $\mu = \mu_r\, \mu_o$ where μ_r is the relative permeability of a medium and μ_o the permeability of a vacuum which has a value of $4\pi\ 10^{-7}$ and is known as the magnetic space constant. If, in this case, the intervening medium is air then μ_r may be assumed to be unity, whence,

$$H = \frac{m}{4\pi \, r^2 \, \mu} = \frac{m}{4\pi \, r^2 \, \mu_r \, \mu_o} = \frac{m}{4\pi \, r^2 \times 4\pi \, 10^{-7}} \; A/m$$

It follows that since the force on a magnetic pole placed in a magnetic field is given by $F = mH$, then the force between two magnetic poles, m_1 and m_2, separated by a given distance (d) will be,

$$F = \frac{m_1 \, m_2}{4\pi \, \mu_o \, d^2} = \frac{m_1 \, m_2}{4\pi \times 4\pi \, 10^{-7} \, d^2} \; N$$

provided that d is expressed in metres required by the S.I. system. In the derived consistent units, and for the reasons stated, the calculation reads as follows,

$$F = \frac{m_1 \, m_2}{4\pi \, \mu \, d^2} \; N$$

$$m_2 = \frac{F \, 4\pi \, \mu_o \, d^2}{m_1} \; Wb$$

$$m_2 = \frac{4 \times 10^{-4} \times 4\pi \times 4\pi \; 10^{-7} \times (6 \times 10^{-2})^2}{3 \times 10^{-6}} \; Wb$$

$$m_2 = 7 \cdot 58 \times 10^{-6} \; Wb$$

The simplicity of the C.G.S. computation is evident, likewise the somewhat greater complexity using S.I. units. The only advantage gained is that the result is compatible with further calculations for which it might be needed in conjunction with electrical units. Since this was not intended and the pole strength, in this instance, was required for its own sake there seems no point to the more complex version. The reader will note how extremely small is the pole strength, namely $7\frac{1}{2}$ millionths of a Weber. Since π^2 features regularly in calculations of this type prospective candidates will be pleased to know that the examining authority have indicated their willingness to accept π^2 as 10. In this case the accuracy obtained by the use of this approximation is maintained to within one ten millionth of a Weber!

This example shows that the move to S.I. units has quite unnecessarily complicated matters. The important point is the *needless* introduction of the change within a *needless* area of study. We must bear in mind that the study of compass deviation and its subsequent elimination is and should be the main concern of the examining authority. It seems therefore

most unfortunate that compass deviation should have added to
it a section of work which is largely superfluous. And then to
adopt the S.I. system within that superfluous part to complicate
the section still further! It is interesting to note that all official
literature on compass work still retains the C.G.S. units, and
so far as *practical* compass work is concerned there are no
charts to date which display the field strength elements in
other than C.G.S. units. It is anticipated that the 1970 charts,
which are not yet published, will give field strengths in A/m.
It is to be hoped that these charts may soon become available
because meantime the 1972 examinations feature certain computations which make use of field strengths expressed in units
appropriate to charts as yet unobtainable. It may be argued
that the position can easily be resolved with a suitable con-
version factor; this begs the question and does not eliminate
the paradox.

Some Questions are Dangerous

Whenever syllabuses are revised and updated there is a
natural tendency to make problems and calculations more
difficult. This is reasonable if the intention is to examine at a
greater depth provided always that the link with practice is
not broken. In compass work the opportunity of breaking
bounds is almost limitless and advantage is often taken to
increase the complexity at the expense of realism. Consider
the case where an effort is made to support a real life situation
by quoting observed deviations aboard ship to have been 'the
same' under two quite different conditions of course and/or
geographic location. Sufficient data is provided for the
problem to be solved but not before it has degenerated to
purely an academic exercise. If deviations were observed they
should be quoted. One can imagine similar types of question
which, although of academic interest, bear no connection with
practice even to the extent that one might say 'this could
never happen'! It would seem wiser to stop before this stage
is reached even though there are many supporters of examination questions which do little more than tease an examinee to
the limit rather than test the competency of the qualifying
officer in matters of theory and practice combined. It is not
always easy to achieve a perfect blend of examination questions;
hitherto the authority setting the examinations has seldom
failed and may be expected to watch for pitfalls as they set out
on the new century of examining.

The Compass Oral Examination—1972

For as long as the writer can remember examinees for Master have been required to demonstrate the practical adjustment of the magnetic compass on the model deviascope instrument. This became accepted routine and was part of the oral section of the examination. Candidates rarely failed this part of the examination and were generally quite proficient at adjusting by the direct method of removing the deviation or by equalising the northward field strength on all headings with the aid of the deflector. The model, invented in 1886 by the late Captain G. Beall, Principle Examiner of Masters and Mates, has stood the test of time in more ways than one. Firstly, it provided the means of examining both the theory and practice of adjustment in a very convenient form. Secondly, the simulation of likely ship disturbing effects was easy and realistic. Thirdly, the instrument provided the means whereby the examiners could question a qualifying officer and receive demonstrable answers by using the model. Lastly, the instrument provided an excellent means for instruction unequalled by any other equipment. From 1972 onward only the last mentioned use remains since the examining authority have dispensed with its services.

Qualifying officers will now no longer be required to make use of the deviascope model except under instruction in navigation schools. When they reach the examination they will be examined instead on the more realistic compass and binnacle familiar to every ship's officer. The examining authority would rightly claim that the change is appropriate in the sense that the real thing is better than a demonstration model. This may be so but one is left to wonder why it has taken the best part of a century to come to that conclusion. Probably there are economic reasons against the cost of renewing outworn deviascopes. The changeover will have the certain effect that many demonstrable details of compass work can no longer be made either by the examiner or the examinee. On balance the examinee tends to gain because the binnacle conceals much from both parties while the model revealed everything and therefore encouraged further question and answer. On this account it is debatable whether the change is an improvement or not. Ideally the use of both instruments is best.

Future candidates for Master do well to appreciate the subtle change that has just taken place. Hitherto the examiners would set one candidate to do the practical work on the model while in another room a second candidate would undergo the seamanship oral. Places might then be exchanged and a useful economy of time incorporated. The new arrangements are not so flexible because the candidate is likely to be examined at the binnacle within the examiner's room. Furthermore, the nature and quality of the examination is somewhat different because greater emphasis is laid upon a comprehensive knowledge of compass equipment and minimum standards required as laid down in M Notice 616/1972 (an updated version of M 417). Candidates must, however, be prepared as before to effect a proper adjustment of the compass in its binnacle by any method required; they must also answer questions upon the substance of the Notice just mentioned together with any related questions surrounding the subject which the examiner might ask in addition. In the light of experience more will be revealed but at the moment the writer believes that this practical part of the examination is unlikely to contain a full and complete adjustment of the compass, requiring at the least two full swings, because this will be very time consuming. The consequence of this will be that examiners will require candidates to exhibit compass wisdom in a confident manner by being able to talk about the subject sensibly. Examiners will be equally quick to detect bad practices based on faulty or half-learned theories. Since this would reflect upon the safety of navigation a bad impression would be created. The candidate must be on his guard. With the increasing number of transmitting magnetic compasses examiners will more than appreciate the penalties suffered when such compasses are not properly adjusted for inclination errors. They will expect candidates to understand the real significance of a gyro breakdown under such conditions and what the effects are likely to be on switching over to TMC, particularly if the latter has to monitor in turn the auto-helm and radar, etc.

1972—Onwards?

Whilst the magnetic compass remains the stand-by equipment aboard ship in the case of a gyro failure it would seem that any examining authority will continue to attach importance to this part of the navigator's competence. For the last hundred years the several authorities have continued to express their interest and concern in compass work. The qualifying officers for their part have demonstrated their competence under examination, but there it has too often rested. Compass-wise they have proved themselves just not 'with it' aboard ship, minorities excepted. In general little or nothing is ever done. One hundred years of teaching, instruction and examination has largely failed to provide the navigator with wisdom to comprehend anything more than checking the deviation! After 100 years the navigator is still the slave of the binnacle; during the next hundred years the relationship stands a chance of being reversed unless, as seems likely, the binnacle will disappear and win on points!

CHAPTER 14

The Father of the Gyro Compass.

The navigating officer is privileged today, compared with his predecessor, to enjoy the use of many sophisticated aids to navigation. It is natural that much is taken for granted because both training and practice have occurred at a time when he has been surrounded by examples of control engineering, closed loops and fail-safe systems. Something has already been written concerning the magnetic compass which is the standard heading reference when all else fails. It is time to turn to the gyro compass which is now so much of the bridge scene that its origins have almost faded.

The Prime Instrument

WHILST courses need to be steered and tracks maintained aboard ship it would seem that a compass of one kind or another remains as the ship's prime instrument of navigation. Although the magnetic compass is the standard heading reference in case of a gyro breakdown, the fact remains that a high percentage of ships nowadays carry a gyro compass. Navigators come to expect a gyro installation and use the extra facilities which it provides; automatic steering, radar and D. F. stabilisation and the added advantage of only a small error from the true meridian. As with many machines, familiarity with the use of the gyro compass on the bridge tends to obscure the principles by which it functions. Yet these must have been understood and applied in the first instance. Certainly most ships' officers have studied these principles and understood them (some, perhaps, only vaguely) but fail to recognise that they have been developed entirely within the present century. It seems appropriate therefore, that contemporary navigators should make the acquaintance of the man who made it possible if only to understand the difficulties which he overcame and the ingenuity which he displayed in solving the basic problems attached to inventing a gyroscopic compass.

Dr. Hermann Anschütz-Kaempfe

There seems to be no question that the late Dr. Hermann Anschütz-Kaempfe was the original inventor of the gyroscopic

The late Dr. Herman Anschütz-Kaempfe, the original inventor of the gyroscopic compass

PLATE I

compass. The several stages in its subsequent development are most ably recounted by his cousin Professor Max Schuler, who worked with him and was a close witness to what went on in the early days.

Dr. Anschütz had no initial intention of building a gyro compass. He first studied medicine and then the history of art. Not wholly satisfied with these pursuits he turned his attention towards polar exploration and in this connection delivered a lecture in 1901 to the Imperial and Royal Geographical Society in Vienna. The 29-year-old scientist proposed a submarine voyage under the arctic ice to the north pole. He contended that the journey to the pole by sledge was too hazardous and that the necessary measuring instruments could not be transported over the ice. The submersible craft seemed to him to provide the answer since it could surface from time to time through the sea ice, check its own position, make geodetic and ice observations, resubmerge and repeat the sequence over the whole polar sea wherever it could penetrate the ice. The fact that this suggestion was made by Dr. Anschütz in 1901 shows how advanced of his time he was since it was not actually achieved until 1958 when the U.S.S. *Nautilus* made its historic voyage across the polar sea submerged. Furthermore, although the polar explorer had critics who considered the proposition too dangerous he was nevertheless most earnest and sincere in his beliefs. These he supported with instruments designed by himself and put to test in northern waters, investigated the light conditions below the surface and considered designs of submarine craft which might be suitable for the purpose.

The Question of a Compass

During the discussion which followed the 1901 lecture the seriously-impaired performance of magnetic compasses in high latitudes was mentioned. Apart from the very weak horizontal field there was also the screening and deviating effects of the hull to be considered. Scientists who were present held the view that the solution to the problem might be found in making use of the properties of a gyroscope.

Early Researchers

It seems that the earliest researches into the behaviour of the gyroscope surround experiments designed to detect the

earth's rotation and to investigate the phenomenon of gyroscopic precession. Newton in 1686 gave a mathematical
description to these phenomena. Both pendulum and gyroscopic behaviour were investigated through the succeeding
years; Serson (England) in 1744, Euler (Germany) 1758,
Bohenberger (Germany) in 1827, Sang (Scotland) in 1836,
Foucault (France) in 1851, Smythies (England) in 1856, Trouvé

FIG. 31
The 1904 gyro compass by Anschütz. It was really a directional gyro.

(France) in 1865 and Lord Kelvin in 1884 all contributed
experimental and mathematical data. Dr. Anschütz discovered
that although the theories were well understood and the work
of investigators such as van den Boss (Holland), Werner von
Siemens (Germany) and Lord Kelvin more than appreciated,
no one had designed a practical instrument which would
display the necessary north settling qualities of a compass. He

therefore set about the difficult task of translating theory to practice and it was in his home town of Munich that Dr. Anschütz invented the first directional gyro compass in 1904. The work took him three years to complete.

The 1904 Gyro Compass

Unlike the constrained Foucault gyros, which were in a sense theoretically north-seeking, the first Anschütz compass possessed three degrees of freedom. The instrument was really a directional gyro. Its virtues lay in the basic solution to the problem of an electrically-driven rotor with its spin axis substantially horizontal, to which was added a gravity weight which precessed the gyro in azimuth at a rate equal and opposite to the vertical earth rate for a given latitude. Trials of the 'GYROSKOP' were carried out on the cruiser *Undine* but, although directional gyros were successful for short periods of time, the 'GYROSKOP' proved inadequate on a long-term basis and became quite unreliable with even the slightest rolling of the ship. Dr. Anschütz wrestled with two fundamental problems; unwanted frictional torques about the gimbal axes, principally the vertical axis around which the vessel would turn, and the unfavourable effects of horizontal accelerations caused by the movement of the craft. These basic difficulties were to occupy the mind of the inventor for a long time to come. The reader will detect that although navigation in very high latitudes requires the use of a directional gyro the general requirements for a north-seeking gyro compass were now being considered apart from their use for polar exploration.

The 1905 Gyro Compass

There exists a patent dated July 11th, 1905 for an improved type of Anschütz directional gyro in which the scientist concentrated on reducing unwanted torque about the vertical axis. Twin gyros mounted upon a single shaft forming the rotor of a DC motor were arranged within a case supported on an horizontal axis within a frame, not unlike the arrangement in a modern Arma Brown compass having spinners attached to each end of the rotor shaft. The vertical support of the frame needed to be friction-free and caused the inventor to propose a float immersed in liquid from which the sensitive element was buoyantly supported. Although practical difficulties emerged and were later overcome the concept of a liquid support in one form or another as suggested in the 1905 patent constituted, at the time, a brilliant innovation. The idea has formed the basis for a large number of modern gyro compasses which have since developed through the years.

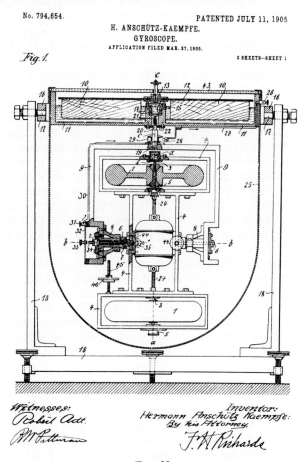

FIG. 32

A working drawing of the improved type of directional gyro, which was patented on July 11, 1905

The Founding of Anschütz & Co., KG

At this time Dr. Anschütz was clearly faced with the necessity of translating the flotation idea into practice and to invent some method of producing a north-seeking instrument out of a purely directional gyro. Léon Foucault, who incidentally introduced the term 'gyroscope' in 1852, pointed the way to a solution by asserting that—'a gyro whose axis is constrained to the horizontal would ultimately precess its axis of rotation into the meridian'. Foucault had no way, at the time, of verifying the statement owing to the absence of the necessary technical means. Some 50 years later Dr. Anschütz became the man to prove the point but not without some financial worries since projects of this nature always cost money.

Finance was sought from the German Navy on the basis that they might reasonably be expected to encourage the development of a compass which no longer depended upon magnetism, particularly since magnetic compasses became increasingly unreliable aboard large warships on account of the deviating forces present. Unfortunately the Navy Ministry were not impressed and refused to help, presumably due to their mistrust of a project initiated by, to them, a complete outsider. Discouraged by the Navy's attitude, Dr. Anschütz tried to solicit help from private individuals and firms but this too was inadequate to permit the work to continue.

Fortunately, Dr. Anschütz made the acquaintance of one Friedrich Treitschke who proved to be young, enthusiastic, full of admiration for the scientist's work and, most important, wealthy. The outcome was the establishing of the firm of Anschütz & Co. in the year 1905 together with an independent research department where the work could proceed under the direction of its industrious leader and backed by its new sponsor.

The 1907 Gyro Compass

In 1906 a further piece of good fortune attended the efforts of the learned Doctor. His cousin, Dr. Max Schuler (at the time not yet fully qualified), was studying mechanics under August Föppl and electro-technology under J. Ossanna in Munich, the former having done much useful work on gyro mechanics, and the latter being credited with introducing alternating current into Germany. Dr. Schuler attended a symposium at the Kiel 'Germania-Werft' and took the opportunity of visiting his cousin. He was soon impressed with the energy and enthusiasm being devoted to the construction of a functional gyro compass. Although Max Schuler had no intention himself of building such an instrument he was certainly not disinterested, recognised the possibilities and, being a mathematician, promised his cousin every assistance. This was to be of great signifiance in the development of the gyro compass and the subsequent liasison between the two scientists became decisive in the matter of its history.

Dr. Max Schuler (later to become Professor Max Schuler in mechanical engineering at Göttingen University) returned to Munich to finish his studies and gain his Diploma at the Technischen Hochschule but not before acquainting his cousin with three most useful suggestions regarding the development of a compass.

(1) He recommended that a considerable increase in the speed of rotation of the rotor should be effected to increase its angular momentum. This demanded an AC instead of DC power unit (after Ossanna).

(2) The gyro should be constructed with a slender spin axis to accommodate the new type of motor and associated spin bearings (after Föppl).

(3) The gyro should be encased in such a way that air turbulence and vortices caused by the high speed of rotation should not exert unwanted torques on the gyro and so impair its basic inertia (after Föppl).

Dr. Anschütz implemented all three suggestions. He rebuilt the AC induction motor by reversing the positions of the rotor and stator, the former being moved outwards to form part of the gyro and the stator inwards to be integral with the surrounding gyro case. The spin axis, quite rigid and slender, penetrated the centre of the stator and the gyro wheel was made to run at 20,000 r.p.m. These innovations were a large step forward in gyro compass design to an extent that many are built to this principle today. Finally, the 1907 compass was the first to employ a gravity control in the literal sense by securing the centre of gravity of the system some 8 cm below the level of suspension. This arrangement accorded with the theoretical views of Léon Foucault some 55 years earlier as the basic condition for a north orientating gyro.

The single gyro compass was supported on a vertical axis by a bell-shaped float immersed in a circular trough of mercury. A downward pointing pin provided the centralised vertical axis against which the system rested with a minimum positive buoyancy.

F

It was to be expected that although the fundamental requirements of a gyro compass had now been understood several practical objections still remained. The scientist O Martienssen pointed out that whilst the 1907 compass might function well in the static conditions of a laboratory

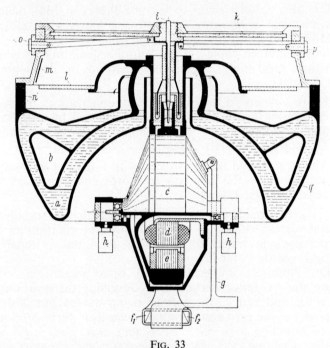

Fig. 33

A schematic drawing of the 1907 gyro compass

it would neither operate successfully aboard ship in a seaway nor when manoeuvring owing to random horizontal accelerations being transmitted to the point of suspension and thereby largely vitiating the action of a pure gravity control. To prevent the incidence of false verticals he suggested that both the point of suspension and centre of gravity should be coincident. These fears were, of course, proved in sea trials which showed up errors of up to 20° on certain courses, a tendency for the mercury to surge and splash and evidence of some drag which prevented the vertical axis from being sufficiently free from friction.

Dr. Max Schuler

At this stage the association between Dr. Anschütz and Dr. Schuler was probably the most significant and fortuitous event which occurred in the initial development of the marine type of gyro compass. Dr. Schuler, when checking the calculations of Martienssen, discovered that the directing property afforded by the gravitational moment applied to the gyro was not the sole cause of error under the conditions of rolling or manoeuvring in a seaway. He discovered that the *period* of the controlled precessional oscillation about the meridian was a more significant factor and wondered if there was a value for this period of oscillation which might tend to reduce the disturbing influences of unwanted horizontal accelerations. Indeed, Dr. Schuler's brilliance produced the answer. If the precessional period of oscillation were made precisely 84 minutes then acceleration errors largely vanished! This unique periodic interval is theoretically established for an imaginary simple pendulum swinging in a uniform and parallel gravitational field whose value is given by $T = 2\pi\sqrt{R/g}$ where the length of the plumb line is the earth's radius (R). It is likewise the orbital period of an earth satellite moving around a smooth earth with no atmosphere at zero height. It may also be considered as the to and fro oscillatory period of a solid object dropped down a shaft bored diametrically through the earth! Although fascinating and apparently irrelevant the same unique period of oscillation would be obtained on the moon if the density of that satellite were the same as that of the earth.

This remarkable discovery was implemented by Dr. Anschütz in 1908 and this gyro compass was satisfactorily tested aboard the German warship *Deutschland* with the result that the compass was produced for the German navy and considerable interest shown by Russia, Italy, Argentina, France and Norway. Some years later Dr. Schuler, while lecturing at Göttingen, tried to apply the same principles to aircraft gyros and although he met with partial success in this field the technical means were insufficient to solve the problem in the air.

Damping the Precessional Oscillations

The sequence of events and the progress made by Dr. Anschütz have not so far included the means by which the built-in oscillations across the meridian were eliminated to

Dr. Max Schuler, who formed a successful partnership with Dr. Anschutz
PLATE II

turn the gyro from a north-seeking element (after Foucault) into a north-settling instrument for use aboard ship. The theory, practice and experiments which had led so far to the solution of a compass naturally caused this aspect to engage the interest of the inventor. He recognised that the east/west amplitude of the oscillation was directly proportional to the vertical amplitude, i.e. the tilt of the sensitive element. Using pressure of air built up within the rotor case he caused this to be channelled circumferentially around the case towards the bottom dead centre position where it was directed westward and issued from twin vents partially covered by a small pendulum shutter pivoted about an east/west axis (Fig. 33). Depending upon the instantaneous tilt the shutter allowed the escaping air to cause a reactionary torque about the vertical axis directed in the opposite sense to the azimuthal drift. The effect of this was steadily to reduce the vertical amplitude of oscillation. This in turn continuously reduced the azimuthal precession rates since these were themselves a function of instantaneous tilt. By this ingenious method Dr. Anschütz contrived a *north-settling gyro compass*; in fact, the first complete compass of its kind—dated 1908. The patience and industry of Dr. Anschütz and his associates, especially Dr. Schuler, had its reward. It earned, for Dr. Hermann Anschütz-Kaempfe, in the writer's view, the just title of 'Father of the Gyro Compass'.

Rolling Errors

It would be unrealistic to suppose that the first complete compass would remain faultless and perform perfectly under all conditions. During 1910 when the German fleet were on exercise it was found that all the single gyro compasses showed similar errors in a heavy swell. This was clearly a severe setback to an instrument which had hitherto proved itself reliable.

The solution to the problem of rolling error was also made by Dr. Max Schuler to whom credit has already been given in respect of the 84-minute period. The scientist pondered the problem, assumed that some mathematical relationship had been overlooked and set out to find it. The result of his work theoretically supported the observed errors and pointed the way to their elimination. It seemed that whenever the assembly was set swinging in either the north/south or east/west planes due to rolling that no errors appeared, but whenever the mode of swinging lay between these directions trouble occurred.

Obviously some concealed effects became cumulatively apparent. Dr. Schuler conceived that a suppression of the swinging in either of the cardinal modes might eliminate the cause of error. To do so about the east/west axis was clearly impossible because the whole operation of the instrument depended upon the detection of tilt about that axis. It was necessary therefore, to effect some form of stabilisation of the

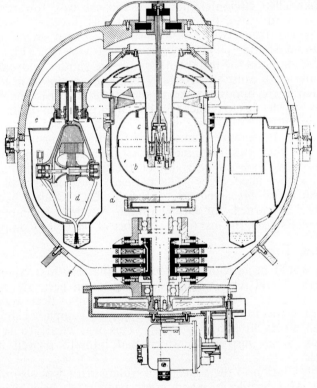

FIG. 34
A schematic drawing of the triple gyro compass

system about the north-south axis. After considering the problem throughout the day, it was late one evening that he hurried to tell his cousin what he had discovered, and the means by which the problem could be solved. Dr. Anschütz listened intently; no doubt with some relief. It was decided to modify the compass forthwith.

The Triple Gyro Compass

In order to prevent the compass swinging in the east/west plane about its north/south axis, Dr. Schuler proposed to make use of the stabilising effect of additional gyros. Two more were fitted such that in plan view the three were located in the pattern of an equilateral triangle with its apex under the 180° mark. The gyro located at this position had its rotation axis orientated in the meridian, while the two additional gyros were located towards the north-west and north-east with their spin axes orientated in the sense 030° and 330° making equal angles each side of the meridian. Each gyro case was pivoted about a vertical axis. The first gyro provided angular momentum in the direction of the meridian, while the second and third which were linked so that their spin axes maintained equal angles from the meridian, contributed a further component of momentum in the line of the meridian and another at right angles to it. The effect of this arrangement was to increase the period of oscillation of the system very considerably in the east/west plane when the ship rolled, thereby reducing the amplitude of the swing and bringing about a stabilisation in this direction. This was essentially the cure for the rolling errors referred to.

Naturally, the curing of one fault often brings further trouble in another direction. In the development of the initial gyro compasses this was no exception and caused the inventors to re-design the flotation system. This consisted of a flotation sphere immersed in mercury, located by a downward-pointing centralising pin. The pendant gyro casings were made gastight and filled with hydrogen to prevent resinification of oil and to disperse heat. Clearly, this substantial reorganisation of the several parts deprived the inventors of the means of using reactionary air jets for damping purposes (since the gyro cases were sealed) and alternative means had to be found to damp out the precessional oscillations each side of the meridian. In any event the damping torques about the vertical axis were not perfect and had the disadvantage of incurring a damping error which increased with latitude.

Damping of the Compass with a Flume Tank

Dr. Anschütz and Dr. Schuler had only one major obstacle to overcome; to substitute the original method of damping with something different. The reader will appreciate that whilst the solution to such a problem now appears simple with hindsight, at the time it required considerable ingenuity and foresight to decide precisely what was required.

Often, in such cases, the ideas and progress made in one area or discipline can help in another. The problem facing the inventors was to substitute initial damping torques about the vertical axis with others about the horizontal axis on the basis that the oscillations should be damped by appropriate

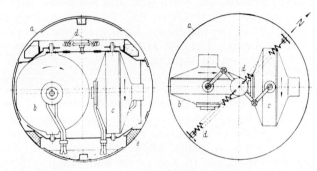

FIG. 35

The twin gyro compass described below

precession rates in the horizontal plane. This entailed damping torques about the same axis (horizontal east/west) used for detecting tilt. Naturally, the applied torques for damping could not be synchronous with those applied to control the compass since this would afford no damping whatever. The specific requirement was the means to phase the damping torques with respect to the main gravity control in such a way that both acted in the same sense at appropriate epochs and opposed each other at intermediate points in time. A non-synchronous form of delayed action was essential. It is at this point that the researches of H. Frahm led to the patenting of flume tanks for the purpose of stabilising the rolling of ships (1910). Dr. Schuler employed the same damping principle for the modified compass by permitting a carefully controlled and restricted flow of oil to accumulate on the north or south side of the instrument at given epochs. The precessional oscillations were, by this means, eliminated with the added advantage that the damping error implicit in the former method was removed, the compass settled in the meridian and was effectively reliable in all latitudes. The success which attended these drastic changes is evidenced by the fact that in 1912 the Anschütz three gyro compass was readopted by the German navy and performed efficiently both aboard warships and merchant ships for some 13 years.

The Twin Gyro Compass

The reader will no doubt be impressed by the steps taken so far to develop the gyro compass. Perhaps the most intriguing of all was the ultimate arrangement adopted for the twin gyro compass used today. Recollect that the first compass had

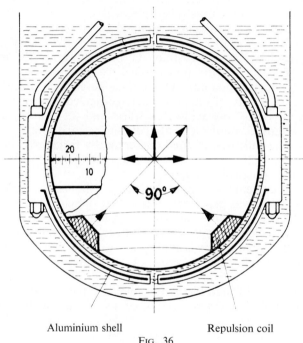

Aluminium shell   Repulsion coil

Fig. 36

the flotation system supporting a single gyro at the centre; the second compass reversed the disposition of the elements with a flotation sphere at the centre supporting three gyros on a frame surrounding the float. Dr. Anschütz now conceived the ideal solution for the sensitive element by placing the gyros *within the flotation element*. This was the third and final transposition of these important elements and remains the basis of all modern Anschütz compasses. Technically this was a brilliant achievement unequalled by any other compass manufacturer to date.

It was soon appreciated that two gyros were sufficient and that the third was superfluous. Provided that the gyros were orientated quadrantally with their spin axes approximately perpendicular to each other then both would contribute components of angular momentum in the line of the meridian as well as in the east/west direction for stability against rolling errors. The two gyros were thus installed *within* a large sphere of approximately 10 inches diameter (25 cm) which constituted the float element. The whole was immersed within a surrounding tank (also spherical) containing acidulated water. Only two problems remained to be solved. The first was to devise the means by which the sensitive element, i.e. the gyrosphere, could sustain its position centrally in the outside container with no physical connection beyond the liquid in which it floated. This was achieved by ensuring that the specific gravity of the gyrosphere coincided closely with the specific gravity of the acidulated water and yet retained a very small negative buoyancy at running temperatures. This tendency to sink was in turn overcome by fitting AC coils in the bottom of the sphere and an aluminium shell in the lower half of the spherical container.

When current was passed through the coil a magnetic repelling force was generated in the shell sufficient to overcome the small negative buoyancy while simultaneously centralising the sensitive element within its container. Alternative methods were investigated but it is interesting to note that the method outlined was the direct result of suggestions made to Dr. Anschütz by no less a person than Professor Albert Einstein, who was an old friend of the inventor and had reached a point in his profound scientific investigations which had become so complex that he had had to cancel all engagements with the exception of a visit to Kiel to see his friend.

The second, and probably final obstacle requiring a practical solution was to convey electric power through the liquid and into the sphere in order to drive the gyros and maintain the repulsion coil effective. Accordingly, Dr. Anschütz arranged two polar-conducting domes at the top and bottom of the gyrosphere and an equatorial conducting band around the middle. Although small losses were inevitable the three phase current flowed through the acidulated liquid along least-resistant paths to these special areas and provided the necessary power for the gyros within. All this was accomplished by the year 1925 during which tests were carried out not only in large warships but torpedo boats, destroyers and smaller craft noted for their violent motion in a seaway. The compass proved satisfactory throughout the trials.

Contemporary Marine Gyro Compasses

The Anschütz compass today makes use of all the developments created by its inventors. Naturally there have been modifications and improvements from time to time but the basic design and concept has remained unaltered. In Europe, Britain excepted, the Anschütz principles of design have been employed in several countries whilst the details of construction only differ slightly. Some compasses have a centre-pin location; only one other a completely free floating gyrosphere, but all feature the twin gyro arrangement within a partially buoyant sphere and each makes use of phased torques about the horizontal axis for damping. Britain and America certainly use similar principles of operation but the technical details are generally quite different in the sense that a single gyro is mostly used with some form of *simulated* gravity control. Japan and Russia have, broadly speaking, picked the best out of both worlds so that 'eastern' compasses often exhibit a mixture of the characteristics of both the 'western' groups. Of course, in all areas many sophisticated compasses have been developed which make full use of modern technology and these are mainly used for special purposes and to provide north-orientated platforms in conjunction with inertial navigation systems and the control of ordnance, etc.

Whatever materialises in the future one can do little better than think of the present in the light of the past. The circuit is complete and the beginning of the gyro compass scene remains with the figure at the centre—Dr. Hermann Anschütz-Kaempfe—the father of the gyro compass which, with the help of others equally dedicated, he invented in 1907. It may be, that in the matter of steering more accurate courses, Dr. Anschütz has materially contributed to safety at sea *internationally*.

CHAPTER 15

The Correction of Speed Error - Variations on a Theme.

The Tilt Detector

MOST officers aboard ship nowadays use the gyro compass for navigating simply because the majority of ships have one. The professional regards it as essential equipment because it is a steadily pointing instrument; it can monitor the radar and D.F. units, steer the ship and performs these functions reliably and with usually only small errors which can be checked easily as a matter of routine.

Perhaps the obvious starting point in any discussion on gyro compasses is to ask—'is it implicit that a gyro compass points true north (or any other fixed direction from which true north may be deduced) and, if not, why not, and by how much does it default under specific conditions'? It is useful to consider this question objectively because therein lies the clue to the means of dealing with it.

All marine gravity monitored gyro compasses possess an extraordinary ability to detect what is called 'tilt'. Gyros which run with their spin axes substantially horizontal detect tilt immediately and with remarkable accuracy. Imagine a gyroscope set with its spin axis horizontal and orientated 090°/270°. It effectively points towards a star at the east point of the horizon (and, of course, to another at the west point) which, in a few moments, rises from the sea and, depending upon the latitude, commences its visible journey across the sky. Those first few minutes reveal the movement very clearly if observed with a sextant; a long slow climb in altitude familiar to every professional. Since the gyro, by virtue of its inertia, is in a sense attached to the stars, it too will tilt east end upward in sympathy with the star to which it points while the eastern horizon rolls away downhill as the earth rotates. So, if the naked eye takes some minutes to watch the star rising, and the sextant reveals the motion in a few moments, the gyroscope does it instantaneously. Whatever may be the circumstances of latitude and azimuth both the gyro spin axis and the star to which it points change their

164

tilt and altitude respectively at a rate which navigators recognise is proportional to the cosine of the latitude and the sine of the azimuth. The rate itself is not so important but the fact that the gyro responds so readily to tilting is fundamental to what follows.

Here then, is the most sensitive of tilt detectors to which may be attached a spirit level, a pendulum, containers of liquid, a steel ball rolling in a trough, a bail weight or any other device which responds to a change from the true horizontal. The response of any such device, if properly applied, can be arranged to exert a real or simulated torque upon the gyro so that it precesses towards the meridian. In the event the result of doing this creates an oscillation of the spin axis to and fro across the meridian which needs to be damped out before the characteristics of a compass are achieved. The details do not matter but it is vital to accept the concept that once the instrument detects tilt, caused by the earth's eastward motion as it rotates, the spin axis of the gyro eventually points towards true north, and rests there in a state of equilibrium. Any subsequent disturbing influence which might upset the equilibrium is immediately detected in terms of minute tilting and the response of the control system until equilibrium is again restored. Sometimes there has been a tendency to quantify the degree or intensity of the gyro compass in its desire to point true north; to use the analogy of the moment of the couple which restores a magnetic compass to the line of the magnetic meridian; or, to determine something called 'directive force'. The reader may spare himself the burden of such ideas and accept, instead, the condition of equilibrium when the spin axis of the gyro is content simply because it doesn't want to point anywhere else! One can speculate, not unprofitably, that when it points true north the rate of tilting is zero and the directive force likewise!

Settling on the Port Beam

It seems therefore, that with a gyro compass the end of the spin axis which tilts *upward* by one means or another responds to a gravitational method of control and reaches a position of equilibrium which lies 90° *to the left of its initial motion*. It is useful to generalise this phehomenon by saying that the upward tilting end of the spin axis points '*to the port beam of resultant motion*'. In this sense the upward tilting end is the eastward-pointing end in the case mentioned, because stars rise in the

east; its subsequent position of rest is, therefore, 000°, i.e.
90° to port of the eastward translation.

Once this concept is accepted there is little difficulty in
considering several alternatives which produce some interesting
results even though they are largely imaginative.   One more
fact is, however, important.   A point on the equator is constantly translated in space, by the earth's rotation, at a speed

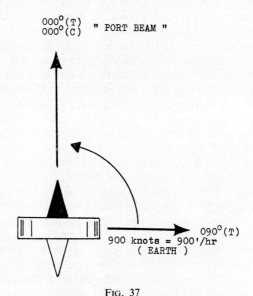

FIG. 37

of 900 knots (360° ÷ 24 × 60), give or take a few knots.   In
other latitudes this speed of translation is 900 cosine latitude
knots, using the principle of parallel sailing with which every
navigator is familiar.   Clearly, the spin axis of an eastward-
pointing gyro tilts upward at the rate of 900' of arc per hour
on the equator; 450' of arc per hour in latitudes 60° N. or S.
(cos 60° = ½) and at other appropriate rates elsewhere.   In
each such case the 'course' is 090° and the compass settles to
the port beam, i.e. 000° (T) (Fig. 37).

Some Flights of Fancy

(i) Suppose the earth were not rotating!   The same effect
could be produced if the craft, supporting the controlled

gyro, were steering 090° (T) at 900 knots! The upward-tilting end of the spin axis would settle to 000° (T), i.e. towards the 'port beam'.

(ii) Keep the earth stationary. Set the craft steering 000° (T) at any realistic or imaginative speed so that the upward-tilting end of the spin axis which points north settles 270° (T), i.e. once more towards the 'port beam'. Clearly, had the craft been stationary the same result would have occurred only if the earth rotated about some axis displaced 90° from the one with which we are all familiar! (Fig. 38).

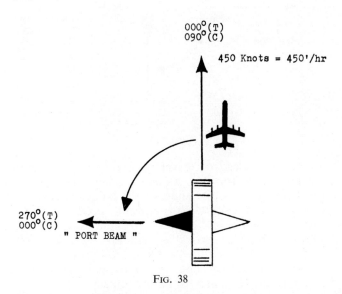

000°(T)
090°(C)

450 Knots = 450'/hr

270°(T)
000°(C)

" PORT BEAM "

FIG. 38

(iii) Revert to the eastward-turning earth. Ship the controlled gyro in an aircraft. Commence a trans-Atlantic flight from Bergen (latitude 60° N.) on a course 270° (T) at 600 knots, which is not unreasonable these days. Consider the controlled gyro spin axis to be initially horizontal and pointing 090°/270°. For the reasons already stated the *eastward* end tilts upward at 450' of arc per hour (900 cos 60°) due to the earth's rotation—but, simultaneously the *westward* end tilts upward at 600' per hour due to the aircraft's progress westward across the ocean. The resultant motion is clearly 150 knots 270° (T), so

that in fact the *westward* end of the spin axis tilts upward
at 150' of arc per hour and the controlled gyro reaches its
equilibrium position pointing 180° (T), i.e. towards the
port beam of the resultant motion! Of course, it might be
claimed that whilst the north end settles south, the south
end settles north and the required condition is satisfied
(Fig. 39). Possibly it is, but the pilot needs to steer 090° (C)
to reach America! The reader will appreciate that owing

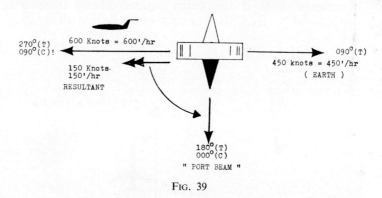

FIG. 39

to the high speed of travel marine type gyro compasses
are unsuitable for this, amongst other, obvious reasons.
Furthermore, this case suggests the unique situation where
the westward progress (a ground speed of 450 knots,
270° (T) is equal and opposite to the eastward translation
provided by the earth; in such an event the resultant
motion is zero, no tilting occurs, the gravitational control
becomes ineffective and the gyro has no position of
equilibrium. It ceases to be a compass.

(iv) Such exaggerated examples, attractive as they are, lead
to the more realistic situations. For instance, using the
aircraft illustration once more, we may imagine the
latitude of Bergen from which an aircraft flies 180° (T)
at 450 knots. Clearly, the upward tilting sensed by the
controlled gyro is again two-fold: the one caused by the
earth's rotation eastward (at 450'/hr.) and the other by
the craft's rotation, around the earth, southward (also
at 450'/hr.). The resultant of these is clearly directed
towards 135° (T) so that the controlled gyro settles once
more 'to the port beam' which now becomes 045° (T),

giving a 45° Low error to be applied before the true
heading can be interpreted. (Fig. 40.)

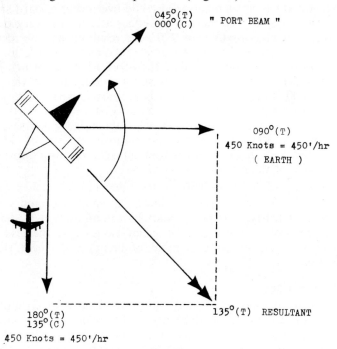

FIG. 40

The Gyro's Dilemma

Perhaps the most interesting fact of all emerges at this
point. The gyro responds immediately to indicate tilting but
it is quite unable to distinguish between the tilting which it
senses due to the earth's rotation and that which is caused by
the supporting craft's own rotation around the earth when it
travels from one place to another. One is tempted to send the
gyro a message—'accept the former, please, but ignore the
latter if you possibly can'!

The Course, Latitude and Speed Error

The examples chosen to illustrate the effect of the two
rotations (ship and earth) emphasise that the gyro as a tilt
sensor can be in serious trouble as a north-pointing compass.
Fortunately ships are relatively slow-moving objects so that
invariably the rate of tilting due to the earth's rotation far

exceeds the rate of tilting due to the north/south component of the ship's rotation around the earth. Nothing like the exaggerated examples mentioned could ever occur aboard ship, but this is not to say there is no effect at all. In every case, except when steering 090° or 270°, the resultant motion of the ship and the gyro compass it carries, is directed a little to the north or south of 090° so that the 'port beam' to which the compass will settle lies a similar small amount to the west or east of 000° (T) *respectively*. This at least tells the navigator that a westerly or high error is associated with all northerly courses; an easterly or low error with all southerly courses. It is a semi-circular error of opposite sign on opposite headings. In all but very high latitudes and on very fast warships the magnitude of the error ($\delta°$) is given by

$$\delta° = 0.064 \text{ V cos } \zeta \text{ sec } \lambda$$

where V is the ship's speed in knots, ζ the course, and λ the latitude. Clearly, it is just a matter of computation to determine the size of the error for given values and there is no difficulty in constructing a table of errors with these three arguments.

The Formula

Whilst the navigator may not take kindly to formulae, unless it is a large one with plenty of haversines, he can hardly complain about the simplicity of the one quoted. It is easy to memorise and anyone can substitute symbols with numbers but the significance of the ingredients can only be appreciated by taking a careful look at them individually—let us do that.

(*a*) The numerical constant, 0.064, is of no concern and is accepted.

(*b*) V denotes the ship's speed in knots. The inference is plain. Double the speed and the error, in degrees, is twice as much. Note that there is a direct relationship here. Stop the ship, or come to anchor and there is no error. All fairly obvious.

(*c*) The speed error is proportional to cosine course. This is vital information. Cosine $0° = 1$, cosine $90° = 0$ and cosine $180° = -1$. The significance is very important: the error is *zero* when heading 090° or 270°; it is *maximum* heading 000° (T) and likewise heading 180° (T) but of *opposite sign*. These points have already been made above. The formula confirms them.

(d) If (b) and (c) are combined and the product, V cos ζ, considered it is clear that this is purely the rate of change of latitude or, more easily, the 'd.lat/hr'. In the gyro compass context this is usually referred to as the ship's

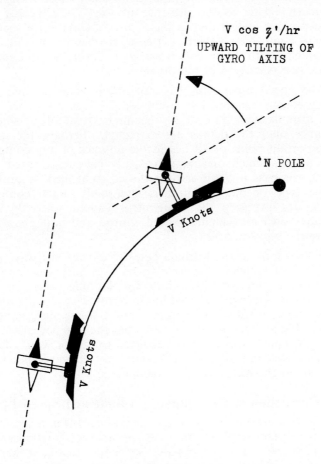

V cos ζ'/hr
UPWARD TILTING OF
GYRO   AXIS

'N POLE

V Knots

V Knots

FIG. 41

'north/south component of motion'. It is, as described above, the rate of unwanted tilting detected by the gyro and over which we could wish that it was not so sensitive! V cos ζ is the mischief maker and has deserved the designers' careful scrutiny (Fig. 41).

(e) The speed error is proportional to secant latitude. This is very important too. Secant $90° = \infty$. The error, whilst present at the equator, increases steadily with latitude until it becomes quite unmanageable in the very high latitudes, a fact which in practice does not affect navigation greatly owing to the presence of ice. Nevertheless, the reader may detect that in the matter of speed error marine gyro compasses perform better when they do not have to contend with *High Speeds* or *High Latitudes*; still more, the one occurring in the other!

(f) The speed error mix has now been analysed and the ingredients examined in some detail. It is no longer just a formula with little or no meaning. It is full of significance once the details are extracted. Perhaps the most important point of all lies in the absence of any compass constants which one might casually have anticipated. If the compass is a tilt sensing device controlled by gravity the type or manufacturer is irrelevant. Each compass features precisely the same error caused solely by the ship's own movement. Speed, course and latitude; these are the only variables.

(g) A final look at the formula helps to explain the ways and means of reducing the error to zero. Clearly, one cannot entertain any special values for latitude which might eliminate the error, at least not in terms of the secant which has no zero value. The term V cos ζ seems more hopeful but this product is only zero if either the ship never moved, or the course was for ever restricted to east or west! Both unrealistic but all the same important conclusions which bear on the methods of correction.

The Correction of the Course, Latitude and Speed Error

Everyone who uses a gyro compass aboard ship is involved with the speed error in one way or another. Usually the manufacturer makes the practice so simple that it is hardly noticed but it is still important that the navigator is aware of what is happening so that at no time will he be misled in the vital matter of heading reference.

There are basically four ways of dealing with the speed error. The first is the obvious one of allowing the compass to settle in the virtual meridian and knowing what the error is, from a suitable table, to make due allowance for it when setting courses or correcting bearings. In other words to do nothing about eliminating the error mechanically or otherwise. This is undoubtedly the simplest way out and certainly the most economic. Before one is tempted to dismiss the idea as of no consequence the navigator does well to remember that he never navigates directly from the master compass but always from steering and bearing repeaters which he usually aligns with the master compass. When he does this he clearly transfers any error (regardless of cause) from the master to the repeaters. If the error is subsequently determined on the bearing repeater it can now be simply reduced to zero by altering the setting. When course (or speed) is altered the speed error naturally changes, because the formula says it must, and the error can be checked again by taking an azimuth. Whatever error appears can once more be eliminated with the repeater setting knob. Meanwhile, the master compass can show any reading it likes because no one uses it directly to navigate. In practice residual errors are usually observed and recorded owing to the difficulty of resetting a repeater when the ship is yawing in a seaway.

The second approach to dispensing with the speed error is the means by which the designers of certain compasses introduce a spurious error of equal amount and opposite sign. This is done by sleight of hand, causing the heading reference to change without influencing the equilibrium position of the gyro. In other words, the gyro spin axis points to the virtual meridian, i.e. to the port beam of the resultant motion, but the lubber's mark and the ring upon which it is engraved is moved artifically by an amount equal to the speed error and in the *same direction*. The effect of this device is to make the compass reading appropriate to a condition where no error exists. A case, as it were, of two wrongs making a right! If the transmitter, i.e. the motor which transfers master compass indication to repeaters, is attached to the moveable lubber ring it can easily be made to move the repeater card by the same amount in the *opposite direction* thereby removing the error from all such repeaters.

A third method of eliminating the speed error amounts practically to the same thing whereby the *card* of the master compass (in Italy they call it the mother compass—*bussola madre;* likewise in Germany—*mutter Kompass!*) is moved directly in the *opposite* sense to the actual speed error, so that the transmitter actuates the repeater motors in the same direction. Each of these devices removes the speed error solely by rotating the graduated compass card of each repeater but none of them interferes with the equilibrium resting position of the gyro spin axis.

This leaves one final method by which the compass designer may eliminate the speed error. The point has been made that the error only occurs because the gyro cannot distinguish between the tilt caused by the ship's north/south component and that produced by the earth's eastward rotation. The fact that the north/south motion of the ship (V cos ζ) is known to the navigator at all times points the way to removing the cause of the trouble at source by anticipating the unwanted rate of tilting. All that is necessary is to apply a couple about the vertical axis of the sensitive gyro and cause it to precess about its east/west axis at the rate V cos ζ in a direction opposing its natural tendency to tilt. This secures the gyro spin axis substantially horizontal as the ship proceeds to the north or south. This term in the formula is thereby made zero, the unwanted tilting removed at source and further embarrassment avoided. Of course, this ideal method of dealing with the speed error requires a carefully controlled torque motor as was used hitherto in the Sperry Mk 20 compass and used today in the Mk 37. Naturally, such arrangements add cost to the equipment and one wonders whether the trouble is worth it, especially since the error is known, is never very great and can be applied easily.

Some Details of Speed Error Correctors

Anschütz Delta Corrector

This is a very ingenious corrector in the sense that the mechanism moves the compass card to the correct reading. It performs this function automatically once the operator sets the ship's speed on a moveable concentric scale against a stationary latitude scale. These scales appear horizontally within the 10° compass card on top of the compass. The setting is made manually with a knob provided for the purpose linked by suitable gearing (Fig. 42).

The effect of making the setting is to turn an horizontal circular disc in which is cut a spiral groove. Two roller bearings on vertical shafts engage with the groove. The bottom ends of the shafts are attached to a sliding carriage fixed to the base plate. The base plate carries the azimuth motor and associated gearing. The sliding carriage moves solely in the direction of the ship's fore and aft line.

The bridge of the sliding carriage has a vertical shaft projecting downwards. At the lower end of the shaft is a sliding block which is set into a sliding lever attached to the inner disc of the azimuth gear. The effect of making the scale setting is to move the bridge of the carriage either forward or aft of the centre of the base plate a predetermined amount and likewise the sliding block within the sliding lever below it. The

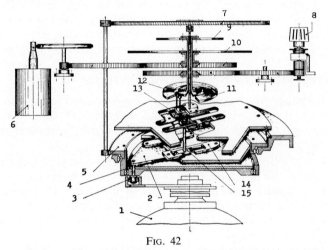

FIG. 42

Key: 1 Follow-up Sphere. 2 Segment Lever. 3 Coupling Block. 4 Inside Disc. 5 Outer Disc/Azimuth Gear. 6 Azimuth Motor. 7 360° Compass Card. 8 Setting Knob. 9 Speed Scale. 10 10° Compass Card. 11 Spiral Groove. 12 Roller Bearings. 13 Sliding Carriage. 14 Sliding Lever. 15 Sliding Block.

sliding lever forms part of an articulated system connected to a segment lever (approximately in the form of a quadrant) which has its corner pivot directly connected to the follow-up sphere lower down. The scale setting, therefore, causes the follow-up sphere to turn in azimuth by the amount of the speed error. The electrical azimuth sensing, operated by this intentional displacement between the gyrosphere and the follow-up sphere, causes the azimuth motor to eliminate the displacement while simultaneously driving the compass cards to their zero error positions.

Part of the ingenuity of the mechanical system lies in the way in which the sliding block moves off centre by an amount equal to the proportion between the ship's speed and the speed of the earth's rotation in the appropriate latitude. When this occurs on courses 090°/270° the articulated lever arrangement does not move the follow-up sphere, but on courses 000°/180° the follow-up sphere is rotated the full amount of the speed error. On intermediate courses the azimuthal rotation is proportional to the cosine of the course.

Throughout the action the corrector system moves the inner section of the azimuth gear and the follow-up sphere to a position displaced from *compass* north by the amount of the speed error, or from *true* north by an amount equal to *twice* the speed error, so that when equilibrium is restored by the azimuth motor the cards indicate the true course, even though they (the cards) are not themselves orientated to true north!

Sperry Mk E 14 Speed Error Corrector

Although this compass is no longer manufactured in this country, it is so well known, and sufficient of them remain, to mention the type of speed corrector which must be familiar to many navigators.

Essentially it also consists of a lever system bolted to the aft end of the inner member or spider element, i.e. part of the frame structure and therefore part of the ship. Its purpose is to move the lubber ring (and thereby the lubber's mark) in the *same* direction as the speed error and so making the compass read the true course.

The sensitive element meanwhile settles to compass north and assumes its speed error direction away from true north.

The action of the corrector system begins with the cosine cam roller which engages with an eccentric groove cut into the underside of the azimuth gear. A bell crank fitted to the other end of the cosine cam arm is attached to the lower arm of the lever system causing it to move about the crosshead adjustable pivot. The remote end of the lower arm has a common pivot which causes the upper arm to move thereby causing the fixed block to communicate this movement to the lubber ring to which they are bolted. They perform this movement via the adjustable block and pivot whose position can be altered by the auxiliary latitude adjustment knob as a *superimposed* correction for the damping error inherent in this type of compass. Two movements are thereby communicated to the lubber ring; the speed error correction and the superimposed latitude correction. Clearly, the extent of lateral movement is governed not only by the cosine cam roller but also by the position of the cross-head adjustable pivot which, by means of the speed error corrector knob, can be moved vertically an amount indicated by the graduation on a sliding latitude scale being made to coincide with the selected ship's speed curve. The reader will no doubt note that in Fig. 43 the aft side of the lubber ring has been moved to port so that the lubber's mark is deflected to starboard, or clockwise, thus affording correction for an easterly combined error appropriate to, in all probability, the ship steering on a southerly course.

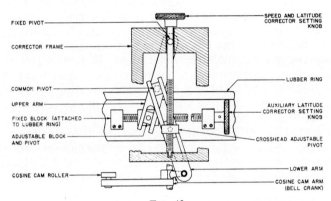

FIXED PIVOT

CORRECTOR FRAME

COMMON PIVOT

UPPER ARM

FIXED BLOCK (ATTACHED TO LUBBER RING)

ADJUSTABLE BLOCK AND PIVOT

COSINE CAM ROLLER

SPEED AND LATITUDE CORRECTOR SETTING KNOB

LUBBER RING

AUXILIARY LATITUDE CORRECTOR SETTING KNOB

CROSSHEAD ADJUSTABLE PIVOT

LOWER ARM

COSINE CAM ARM (BELL CRANK)

FIG. 43
Speed and latitude corrector mechanism

This type of corrector was preceeded by an interesting alternative mechanism used on the Admiralty Sperry compass of some years ago. A cosine ring or groove was cut into the vertical wall of the inner member. A pivoted arm engaged a roller bearing within the groove. The pivot consisted of a shank and ball moving within a cylinder along the axis of the pivot arm. As the ship turned in azimuth the cosine groove and roller bearing moved vertically in proportion to cosine course. This vertical movement was translated into an horizontal movement by means of a ratchet, gear and quadrant mechanism thereby moving the lubber ring about its vertical axis the proper amount of the error. A scale setting in terms of the maximum error (on 000°/180°) in tenths of a degree, obtained from a table giving this value, was made and this controlled the position of the shank and ball within the pivot arm appropriate to the speed and latitude. No attempt was made in these Mk 14 type compasses to eliminate the error at source; the correction was purely a deflection of the lubber ring to which was attached the transmitter which turned all repeaters in the opposite direction.

The Arma Brown Speed Error Corrector

The speed error, as mentioned above, is eliminated at source in this compass. The navigator has only to set the speed scale on the front panel of the compass. This injects a correction signal proportional to $V \cos \zeta$ into the azimuth servo loop thereby creating a couple about the vertical axis, through the vertical torsion wires, which precesses the sensitive gyrosphere about its east/west axis at the rate of unwanted tilt due to the north/south component of ship's motion. The cosine function of the course derives from the synchro transmitter because the voltages induced in the transmitter stator windings are proportional to cosine course. The reader may note that the emphasis now lies towards creating the required torquing couples through signal voltages of the correct order so that the unwanted effects of the ship's motion can be anticipated in advance and got rid of before they cause mischief. None of the elaborate lever mechanisms are then required, nor do they need to rotate either the lubber's mark or the compass cards to give the *appearance* of eliminating the error.

The Navigator

As with any piece of mechanical equipment a wise man reads the instructions and obeys them. Navigators using one gyro compass or another do the same and set the several correctors provided. Failure to do this, or to make the necessary adjustments *en route* simply invites the gyro to do some unwanted tilting and so to cast a doubt on the heading reference until error observations are taken during normal bridge routine. In congested waters, or areas which demand special care in navigating, the officer of the watch has the speed corrector properly set in the knowledge that, permanent errors excepted, he has available the closest approach to true north orientation of which the gyro equipment is capable.

Qualified officers with experience barely need reminding of these things. On the other hand qualifying officers need to recognise that the D.o.T., whose acquaintance they will one day renew, are very inquisitive about the speed error and need to be certain that the man on the bridge knows what it is all about. That way lies another step to greater safety at sea.

CHAPTER 16

How's She Heading?

The success of every passage depends upon the accuracy of the courses steered. When the ship is set upon her course can it be that certain factors are overlooked and even taken for granted?

OF the thousands of ship navigators there surely can be only a small minority who would question their belief in the accuracy of the ship's course at any given instant. Normally the facts are simple and provide little reason for doubt. The intended true course is known from the chart, the magnetic or gyro errors are found by routine observation, applied, and the compass course is steered accordingly. Within the process certain allowances may have been made to counteract the influences of wind, tide or current, but these are standard procedures and only determine the course to be steered by compass. And yet there is one salient feature upon which the accuracy of everything depends—the position of the *lubber's line.* To doubt that this small mark, located within the bowl of every magnetic compass and engraved on the verge of every gyro repeater, should not represent the bow of the ship hardly crosses the mind of the navigator aboard ship. It is one of those small things which is taken for granted. In fact one can go further by saying that the location of the lubber's line is so firmly identified with the ship's head that the navigator considers it entirely irrelevant to suggest otherwise. The assumption is almost complete. But not quite, because the writer questions it seriously and invites the reader's attention while he reconstructs what so often happens on the bridge.

Setting up the Gyro

Contemporary practice justifies our considering the use of the gyro compass first because the magnetic compass has largely lost its position as the standard heading reference except in cases where no gyro is fitted.

Let us suggest a possible and likely sequence. The ship is alongside the quay and the master compass is shut down either for maintenance, repair or because the period in port justifies closing the machine down, even though some compasses benefit from continuous running. Some hours before sailing the master compass is restarted. If the ship has not been moved since the compass was stopped then the indicated heading will remain substantially unaltered and will be the heading upon which the master compass will finally settle. In such a case the officer in charge has little to do once the compass has been put through the starting routine and is set to 'run'. In the event of the ship having been moved from berth to berth during the time the compass was stopped the navigator will have either preset the master compass by one means or another to the approximate ship's head derived from a magnetic compass corrected for a known or assumed error, or will have started the compass irrespective of heading and allowed it sufficient time to settle.

In each case, and after a suitable settling period has elapsed, the navigator will align each of the repeaters to the master heading and await sailing time. It is submitted that the confidence displayed in this routine is to an extent misplaced because it assumes that the lubber's line of the master compass marks the true fore and aft line through the centre of the compass—that the master compass has no error inherent to itself—and that the lubber's line at each of the repeaters Nos. 1, 2, 4 and 5 all mark the fore and aft line of the ship through the centre of each repeater bearing plate. The confidence is therefore misplaced to the extent of no less than six unwarranted assumptions! And yet this is what is so frequently done.

What Does the Gyro Error Mean?

At this point one should consider the accuracy of the heading reference at the various positions.

(1) At the *master compass* any error in the settling heading is due to:—

(a) An inherent permanent error of the master compass itself; or, an error due to maladjustment of one or other of the corrector systems provided.

(b) An error caused by the lubber's line of the master compass being displaced a fractional amount (sometimes as much as 2° and 3°) to port or starboard of the fore and aft line through the centre of the compass.

(2) At each of the *bearing repeaters* Nos. 1, 2, 4 and 5 any error is due to:—

    (*a*) An inherent permanent error of the master compass.

    (*b*) A displacement of the master compass lubber's line.

    (*c*) A displacement of the lubber's line of *each* of the repeaters Nos. 1, 2, 4 and 5.

(3) At the *steering repeater* No. 3 any error of heading reference is due to:—

(*a*) An inherent permanent error of the master compass.

(*b*) A displacement of the master compass lubber's line.

N.B.—No error due to displacement of the lubber's line on No. 3 steering repeater itself because this is only a reference mark. It makes no pretence to indicate precisely the fore and aft line of the ship as is the case on each of the bearing repeaters Nos. 1, 2, 4 and 5. In fact the steering repeater is often a near vertical dial not even located on the fore and aft centre-line.

Have We Forgotten Anything?

Having assumed too much and too often already, it seems that quite an innocent routine aboard ship has thrown considerable doubt upon the validity of the heading reference at no less than six different locations around the bridge. If confidence has been shaken, may we know the worst? Has anything further been omitted? Let us enumerate and amplify.

(1) The discussion has not taken into account what are called gimballing errors which affect the heading reference. The subject is complex and need not be discussed further because fortunately such errors are minimised or removed in design. In any case the navigator aboard ship can do nothing about them.

(2) No account has been taken of gyro compasses which feature on the one hand 'horizontal azimuth indication' and on the other what is called 'deck-plane azimuth indication'. The terms speak for themselves but the navigator may be unaware with which type he is dealing. For example, the Sperry MkE 14 and the Brown types A and B gyro compasses indicate azimuth in the *horizontal plane* and cause no concern. Many of these compasses are in use afloat although they are no longer manufactured.

On the other hand the Sperry Mks. 30 and 37, and the Arma Brown compass all indicate azimuth in the *plane of the ship's deck*. This, of and by itself, can incur an error of the order of 2° in the inter-cardinal heading reference if the ship has a 30° list. It would on this account be unwise to align repeaters with the master compass under these conditions though no great harm would be done because the error would disappear when the ship became upright. The point is made however, if for no other reason that most officers are unaware of such limitations.

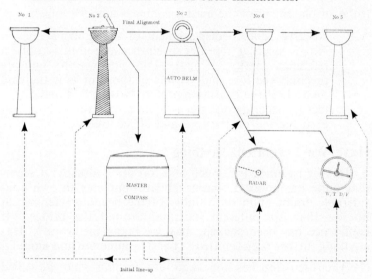

FIG. 44

(3) Whatever uncertainties exist regarding the accuracy of the lubber's line at the master compass these are repeated at both the radar and W/T D/F installations whenever these are stabilised with reference to true north. In other words stabilisation is effected to a presumed and not accurate datum direction. It follows that true courses and true bearings derived from either of these instruments can be in error although they have been presumed to be accurate.

Can Order be Restored?

Returning to practice, let one bearing repeater be selected upon which to observe the error, say No. 2 repeater. Before doing this, however, check its lubber's line. With a centre-line repeater there is no difficulty because the lubber's line can be sighted with the azimuth mirror on the centre of the mast; if there is no mast, on the bow itself. If the repeater is displaced to one side or the other from the fore and aft centre-line careful measurements must be taken to ascertain what this displacement is and a mark made near the bow which reproduces the displacement accurately. If any inaccuracy of the repeater lubber's line is detected it must be eliminated by slewing the repeater using the slotted holding down bolts, if fitted, for the purpose.

Once the lubber's mark has been accurately aligned with the ship's fore and aft line an error is taken in the usual way. Assuming that this has been done on No. 2 bearing repeater the observed error is the amount by which the bearing plate is displaced from true north and since the lubber's line has been checked it is also the error of the ship's head on No. 2 repeater. The navigator can now reset the bearing plate of No. 2 repeater until the true and compass bearings of the sun, say, are the same. No. 2 repeater is now correctly orientated with zero error and the heading reference is also correct.

Next, re-align repeaters Nos. 1, 3, 4 and 5 to indicate this heading. Since repeater No. 3 is used only for steering purposes in the wheelhouse it is now indicating the correct true heading and the auto-helm can be set to the course required. The radar and D/F can now be aligned to No. 3 steering repeater so that each is now correctly stabilised. Any attempt to stabilise either the radar or the D/F in a casual manner with the nearby steering repeater *before* it has been properly checked should be seriously avoided. Repeaters Nos. 1, 4 and 5 are now indicating the same as No. 2 repeater *but their individual errors are not necessarily zero* because their respective lubber's lines may be displaced similar fractional amounts one way or the other. Repeaters Nos. 1, 4 and 5 if used for taking bearings or setting courses cannot be relied upon for *either* purpose!

Errors must now be taken *individually* on repeaters Nos. 1, 4 and 5 and then reduced to zero be reorientating the bearing plates of each. These repeaters are now correctly orientated with reference to true north and can be used for taking bearings. Any discrepancy of heading reference on each of repeaters Nos. 1, 4 and 5 will indicate the misalignment of the respective *lubber's lines*. This is most likely at the wing repeaters but since it is unlikely that *courses* will be set from these repeaters

their inaccuracies of heading reference can be tolerated.
Nevertheless, for those who desire overall accuracy the lubber's
lines of repeaters Nos. 1, 4 and 5 should be checked *before*
observing the several individual errors. In this way repeaters
Nos. 1, 2, 4 and 5 all have zero error with reference to true
north and each repeater, including steering repeater No. 3,
indicates the true ship's head.

At this point *and not before*, the adjustable lubber's line
(if fitted) on the master compass should be set to show the
same heading as repeaters Nos. 1, 2, 3, 4 and 5. If the lubber's
line cannot be so adjusted then the whole master compass, e.g.
the Arma Brown gyro compass, must be reorientated the
required amount. It must be pointed out that this does not
mean that no permanent error exists on the master compass,
but it does mean that whatever error it does possess is equal
and opposite to the amount by which its own lubber's line is
displaced from the ship's fore and aft line. To make this
point clear, suppose No. 2 datum repeater reads 204° clear
of all error with the lubber's line properly aligned. At the
same time the master compass fortuitously indicates 204° also.
If the lubber's line was assumed to be properly aligned and
there was a known (?) permanent error of 1° high the compass
would read 205°. Since it actually reads 204° this means that
the lubber's line was displaced 1° to port of the fore and aft
line, causing an error of 1° low. The compensating errors are
of opposite sign and make the determination of either the one
or the other virtually impossible. In the event one might
assume that a permanent error on the master compass is
unlikely; this provides a means of locating the lubber's line of
the master compass as close to the fore and aft line as it is
reasonably possible to get.

Reversing the Order

The reader will note that, whilst it is normal procedure to
work from the master compass outwards towards each of the
repeaters on the basis that it is the master compass which is
the initial datum, this sequence should be reversed at the first
opportunity once an error on the bearing repeater has been
obtained. This is, of course, quite fundamental because the
only feature in any such sequence which is not in dispute is the
Sun's true azimuth. It seems almost a platitude to make this
point but it is surprising how many navigators persist in doing
many of the right things in the wrong order. Furthermore, it

is common practice for the gyro compass error to be retained, recorded, and applied to every bearing taken and every course steered. For what peculiar reason is this done when by turning a knob half a turn or so the error can be eliminated? There is no virtue in retaining an error when it isn't wanted!

Installing a Master Gyro Compass

Much of this discussion relates to the correct positioning of the lubber's line particularly at the master gyro compass. Installing engineers seldom have much regard to this point and are still less frequently assisted by navigating officers at the time of installation. In practice a fair approximation is the most that can be hoped for by using the fore and aft trend of the deck seams, if any. A more portable instrument (for example, an Arma Brown compass) is orientated approximately with reference to the fore and aft edge of a bench or chart table. Little fault can be ascribed to the installing engineer. It's not really his job but more that of the navigators aboard. In fact to project the true fore and aft line across a master gyro compass which is being installed in a secluded position aboard ship is no easy matter as anyone who has attempted it must know.

The Seeming Paradox

Fortunately, there is in fact no need for the *master compass* lubber's line to mark the fore and aft line precisely. This may astonish the reader after all that has been mentioned. But let this be made very clear before any doubt arises. We are referring now to the *master compass* and not the bearing repeater. The only reason for the master compass lubber's line to be located approximately in the fore and aft line is to provide a proper correction for the course and speed error. This function is dealt with variously in different types of compass but each one has part of its mechanism which relies upon an automatic interpretation of the cosine function of the course. It follows that such mechanism must rely upon the compass being reasonably, but not necessarily accurately, orientated with respect to the ship's fore and aft line. On a compass which bears no such course unit, a Brown type A, and is not used solely for steering the ship, it becomes immaterial where the lubber's line points! Immaterial in the theoretical sense only, because ultimately a navigating officer would

G

be disconcerted if the master compass lubber's line bore no relation (except some fixed number of degrees) to the ship's head. The precise displacement could, however, in fact soon be found as suggested above but the magnitude could be anything instead of the anticipated 1° or 2° at most! The seeming paradox is thus explained. The master compass need not be perfectly aligned within the gyro room but it should approximate the fore and aft line so that cosine resolvers and similar mechanisms can continue to operate for their designed purpose. Apart from this every azimuth check and lubber's line verification should stem from one selected and convenient *bearing repeater* and be *traced backwards* and *terminate at the master compass*. In case it should be thought that this procedure must be repeated every time the gyro is started this is obviously not necessary. Once all the lubber's lines have been verified then all repeaters are aligned to the corrected No. 2 repeater and that is an end to it.

Comparison of Compasses

On many ships it is standard practice when taking an error to do this on the gyro bearing repeater and then to compare the standard and steering magnetic compass headings with that of the repeater and thus obtain the errors on the magnetic compasses and subsequently the respective deviations. Great caution should be exercised in such a sequence because once again the accuracy of the lubber's lines of probably two magnetic compasses as well as that of the bearing repeater is involved. If none of these have been previously checked then comparisons of ship's head are quite pointless. Unfortunately printed deviation journals often display columns marked 'gyro heading', 'standard compass course', and 'steering compass course' with further columns for the respective deviations. Thus, navigators are encouraged to record by comparison deviations the accuracy of which can be in considerable doubt. The writer suggests that there is no efficient substitute for actually taking the error on the standard magnetic compass separately. There is also further objection to the method of obtaining errors by comparing ship's head references when dealing with several compasses and this lies in the fact that it is very easy to make a mistake in naming the several errors, especially if one compass has an error of opposite sign to another. In short, the method of comparing compass headings is a lazy man's method, assumes unwarranted accuracy of the lubber's lines, encourages mistakes and often leads to spurious errors being recorded and subsequently used.

Alignment

If part of the navigator's discipline is to steer a correct and proper course clear of obstruction then it would seem that the heading reference at every position where it is displayed should be accurate and that errors should be ascertained with equal care and subsequently removed whenever possible. The only single feature which precludes the perfect alignment of all compasses aboard ship is magnetic variation. The magnetic compasses should therefore be the only ones displaced by this amount. All gyro repeaters should show the same true heading and exhibit zero error. Only by these means is it possible to justify the proper use of the ship's prime instrument of navigation and to answer confidently the familiar question—'How's she heading?'

AFTERTHOUGHT

WHILST the foregoing topics are restatements of existing knowledge and information, one hopes that the reader may have absorbed more of the atmosphere surrounding his compass equipment. It is said that in some peculiar fashion a horse and its rider come to appreciate each other even though neither speak the same language. At least both have the advantage of being animate. For a navigator to cultivate an affection for his compass in quite the same manner would seem to be the first sign of madness; but if the officer on the bridge, the master of his ship or the owner of his private boat gains an understanding of his compass equipment which does not go beyond theoretical genius on the one hand nor practical casualness and unconcern on the other, then he will come that much closer to being a navigator for whom his compass, whatever its type, is probably the most practical and important part of his navigational equipment. Perhaps the art of navigation is to know where you are going; a navigator with a close affinity for his compass knows where he is heading more confidently than those without.

J. K.

INDEX

A

A, coefficient, apparent, 73
A, coefficient, causes, 71
A, coefficient, how to find, 71
A, coefficient, real, 72
Adjusting, compasses, 22
Airy, Sir George, F.R.S., 79
Azimuth Mirror, test for, 75

B

B, coefficient, adjuster's problem, 37
B, coefficient, due to Flinders bar, 99
B, coefficient, Home Coast procedure, 44
B, coefficient, separation, 36
B, coefficient, tentative separation, 43
Bearing reference, 5, 10
Binnacle, 23

C

Coefficient, *see* under letter
Compass, adjustment, 22
Compass, alignment, 179
Compass, badly adjusted, 32
Compass, examinations, 133
Compass, errors, observing, 51, 68, 70
Compass, heading comparisons, 51, 186
Compass, licking into shape, 28
Compass, oral examination, 143
Compass, standard, 50
Compass, transmitting, 3, 5, 35, 62, 97
Compass, unsteadiness, 30, 35, 64, 97, 109
Compass, well adjusted, 33
Correctors, interaction between, 98
Correctors, order of placing, 88
Correctors, magnetic compass, 88
Course, to check, 9

D

D, coefficient, correction, 92, 103
D, coefficient, of Flinders bar, 88, 95
Deviation, accuracy of observed, 4, 70
Deviation, apparent, 73
Deviation, case for small, 17

189

Sphere correctors, 27, 92, 102, 105
Spheres, magnetic field due to, 112
Sphere, single, correction, 111
Sphere, tests for, 112

T

Tests, for azimuth mirror, 75
Tests, for spheres, 112

U

Units, S.I. in magnetism, 138

V

Variation, 7, 69
Variation, setting control, 4, 74

X

X, component, 117

Y

Y, component, 117

Z

Z chart, 39
Z, component, 117